Independent Schools
Examinations Board

GEOGRAPHY
ISEB Revision Guide
(Third edition)

Belinda Froud
Edited by Simon Lewis

Independent Schools
Examinations Board

www.galorepark.co.uk

GALORE PARK

Published by ISEB Publications, an imprint of Galore Park Publications Ltd
19/21 Sayers Lane, Tenterden, Kent TN30 6BW
www.galorepark.co.uk

Design and typesetting Typetechnique

Printed in the UK by Charlesworth Press

ISBN-13 978 0 903627 68 9

First edition published 2005
Second edition published 2007
Third edition published February 2008, reprinted May 2008,
September 2008, 2009, revised October 2009, reprinted 2010, 2011

Details of other ISEB Revision Guides for Common Entrance, examination
papers and Galore Park publications are available at www.galorepark.co.uk

About the author

Belinda Froud has been Head of Geography at Thomas's School, Clapham since 2001. She formerly taught at Broomfield School, Southgate. In her spare time she enjoys pottery, walking up hills and skiing. She believes that Geography is a subject that everyone can enjoy due to its diversity of themes and that lessons should be fun and full of fieldwork.

Acknowledgements

I would like to dedicate this book to the pupils of Thomas's Clapham since 2001. They have worked incredibly hard, achieving fantastic Common Entrance results and a huge percentage have reached the dizzy heights of Top Geographer status! Thanks go to them for their constant ideas on how the guide could be improved and updated. Finally, sincere thanks go to Simon Lewis, my editor.

Updated edition October 2009

 This book has been updated to suit the interim Common Entrance Geography syllabus published by ISEB in October 2009 for first examination in Spring 2011. To cater for pupils taking exams prior to this change, material for the previous syllabus has been retained but with this symbol (plus a grey line in the margin) denoting that such material will no longer be examined in 2011.

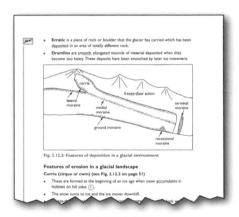

This symbol is used throughout the book for whole pages of text. Where single sentences and smaller amounts of text, for example, in the case of location knowledge maps, chapter summaries, questions and glossary terms, material no longer to be examined in 2011 has been reproduced in *italics* and the 2011 symbol and the line is used to draw your attention to these items on the page.

Current pupils should be aware that **all material in this book** is examined up to the **2010 Summer exam**.

 The small amount of material added to the 2011 syllabus is available to download from www.galorepark.co.uk and this symbol has been used in the text to denote where it is required. The relevant pages are 15, 71 and 96.

Contents

Remember: sections in *italics* will **not** be examined from Spring 2011.

Introduction

I hope that you find this guide as useful as the pupils of Thomas's Clapham have over the past seven years. Try to look after your guide; it will be a vital aid before your Common Entrance examination. However, it will not only be of use in your revision period but also during lessons and homework times.

Included in the 'Test yourself' section at the end of each chapter are glossary lists which you should complete as you study the different themes. Also use the blank pages to make notes during the study of the examples your teacher has chosen. Ask your teacher to check that you have filled the glossary lists in correctly. I have included some example Common Entrance questions for you to try during your revision period. There are two sets of global location maps, one set have all the necessary places marked on and the other set are blank for you to practise marking on the locations.

 More sets are available as downloads from the Galore Park website: www.galorepark.co.uk

Bring this guide to all lessons and keep it with you as often as possible, so that you can make the most of any free minute or two (on the bus, in the bath, etc.). Remember that the best way to learn global location is to test your family. A Christmas global location quiz is always enjoyable; you may even shock your parents at how much you know (and how little they know)!

You may find it useful to make revision cards; the examples, which your teacher has chosen, could be different from those in this guide (see also some suggestions in *Study Skills* by Elizabeth Holtom published by Galore Park). Try to fit all of the information (in bullet point form or as mind maps) onto a card; add all of the necessary maps or diagrams. Make sure that you know the location of the examples.

If you are unsure of any topic area remember to ask your teacher for help.

I do wish you all the best of luck in all of your examinations and remember that you can be a Top Geographer!

The syllabus and your exams

If you are taking your exam before Spring 2011, it will have two sections: one which tests the five themes (and Ordnance Survey skills) and one which tests your knowledge of case studies. Take care; in the case study section there will be **three** questions and you will need to answer **two** of these. The case study section will have questions which require extended writing. Questions on global location could appear in either section. You should read all of this book as you could be examined on any material in it.

2011 This guide has been revised for the new Common Entrance syllabus which will be examined from Spring 2011 onwards. If you are taking this exam from this date, it will have three sections: one which tests Ordance Survey skills, one which tests your knowledge of geographical themes and one which tests global location. When you see this symbol, you can ignore all the text with a grey line next to it in the margin; you will no longer be examined on this material. You can also ignore any text in italics in the location knowledge maps, chapter summaries, questions and glossaries.

There are a few occasions where you will need to know extra material for the exams from Spring 2011 onwards. These are shown when you see this symbol. Your teacher should give you this extra material or you can download it from www.galorepark.co.uk

If in doubt, ask your teacher how to use this book and exactly what you should learn.

Tips on revising

Get the best out of your brain

- Give your brain plenty of oxygen by exercising. You can revise effectively if you feel fit and well.

- Eat healthy food while you are revising. Your brain works better when you give it good fuel.

- Think positively. Give your brain positive messages so that it will want to study.

- Keep calm. If your brain is stressed it will not operate effectively.

- Take regular breaks during your study time.

- Get enough sleep. Your brain will carry on sorting out what you have revised while you sleep.

Get the most from your revision

- Don't work for hours without a break. Revise for 20-30 minutes then take a five-minute break.

- Do good things in your breaks: listen to your favourite music, eat healthy food, drink some water, do some exercise and juggle. Don't read a book, watch TV or play on the computer; it will conflict with what your brain is trying to learn.

- When you go back to your revision review what you have just learnt.

- Regularly review the facts you have learnt.

Get motivated

- Set yourself some goals and promise yourself a treat when the exams are over.

- Make the most of all the expertise and talent available to you at school and at home. If you don't understand something ask your teacher to explain.

- Get organised. Find a quiet place to revise and make sure you have all the equipment you need.

- Use year and weekly planners to help you organise your time so that you revise all subjects equally. (Available for download from www.galorepark.co.uk)
- Use topic and subject checklists to help you keep on top of what you are revising. (Available for download from www.galorepark.co.uk)

Know what to expect in the exam

- Use past papers to familiarise yourself with the format of the exam.
- Make sure you understand the language examiners use.

Before the exam

- Have all your equipment and pens ready the night before.
- Make sure you are at your best by getting a good night's sleep before the exam.
- Have a good breakfast in the morning.
- Take some water into the exam if you are allowed.
- Think positively and keep calm.

During the exam

- Have a watch on your desk. Work out how much time you need to allocate to each question and try to stick to it.
- Make sure you read and understand the instructions and rules on the front of the exam paper.
- Allow some time at the start to read and consider the questions carefully before writing anything.
- Read all the questions at least twice. Don't rush into answering before you have a chance to think about it.
- If a question is particularly hard move on to the next one. Go back to it if you have time at the end.
- Check your answers make sense if you have time at the end.

Tips for the Geography exam

- *Remember that you need to answer two out of the three questions in section B.*
- Look at the number of marks available, in order to assess how much to write.
- Remember that marks are given for the level of detail. If you answer the questions with a high mark allocation in bullet points, you must make sure that the bullet points are extended fully.
- Always read the questions carefully, underlining, circling or highlighting key words or phrases.
- Do not leave blanks. If you do not know the answer, take an educated guess. Wrong answers do not lose marks.
- Make sure that all diagrams are clearly annotated (labelled with explanations).

- Look carefully at the resources given, e.g. maps, graphs, etc.; they will always help you answer the question. (Remember the 'line' on a climate graph is the temperature and the 'blocks' are the rainfall.)
- Include impressive **geographical terms** from the glossary lists whenever possible.

For more tips on how to get the best from your revision and exams, see *Study Skills* by Elizabeth Holtom, published by Galore Park.

Useful resources

Study Skills by Elizabeth Holtom, ISBN: 9781902984599

So you really want to learn Geography Book 1 by James Dale-Adcock, ISBN: 9781902984728

So you really want to learn Geography Book 1 Answer Book by James Dale-Adcock, ISBN: 9781902984735

So you really want to learn Geography Book 2 by James Dale-Adcock, ISBN: 9781905735273

So you really want to learn Geography Book 2 Answer Book by James Dale-Adcock, ISBN: 9781905735280

Revision Crosswords for Common Entrance and Scholarship Geography by Simon Lewis, Download: D0316111

All available from Galore Park: www.galorepark.co.uk

Revision glossaries

These are the first two in a number of glossaries you will find throughout this book in the Test Yourself sections at the back of each chapter. They will help you to see how much you know about the different geographical terms so that you can start to remember them and use them in your exams. This first glossary is all about OS mapwork. Begin your revision by filling in this glossary list in pencil and ask your teacher to check you have filled it in correctly.

OS mapwork glossary

compass . . . .

contour line . . . .

drainage . . . .

easting . . . .

escarpment . . . .

estuary . . . .

grid reference . . . .

key . . . .

knoll . . . .

northing . . . .

plain . . . .

plateau . . . .

relief . . . .

ridge . . . .

symbol . . . .

vegetation . . . .

Fieldwork and general glossary

Now try this second glossary all about fieldwork and more general geographical terms. Again, fill it in in pencil and ask your teacher to check you have filled it in correctly.

annotate ....

continent ....

describe ....

explain ....

fieldwork ....

graph ....

hemisphere ....

human map ....

percentage ....

physical map ....

primary information ....

secondary information ....

Chapter 1: Weather and climate

- **Weather** – the hour-to-hour, day-to-day condition of the atmosphere (wind speed, wind direction, temperature, humidity, sunshine, type of precipitation).

- **Climate** – the average weather conditions for a place over many years – often shown on a climate graph.

- **Microclimate** – the local climate of a small area.

1.1 Microclimates

Factors which affect microclimate

- Physical features – e.g. hills, lakes, valleys.

- Aspect – the direction which a slope or wall faces; south-facing is warmest.

- Wind direction – in the UK a northerly wind will be cold.

- Proximity to buildings – buildings release heat and can provide shelter, thus increasing temperatures.

- Surface – dark surfaces absorb heat.

- Distance from the sea – in winter, places near the sea are warmer.

Comparison of urban and rural microclimates

Urban

- One degree warmer than rural areas in the day.

- Four degrees warmer than rural areas at night (tarmac absorbs heat in the day and releases it at night).

- Release of man-made heat from power stations, houses, cars, etc.

- Less wind than in rural areas; tall buildings act as wind breaks; however, funnelling can cause gusts.

- More convectional rainfall; warmer than rural areas.

- Less snow.

Rural

- Affected by the shape of the land – south-facing slopes are warmer.

- Valley floors are cold at night due to cold air sinking, sometimes causing frosts.

- Often stronger winds – little shelter.

1.2 Instruments

Temperature is measured in degrees centigrade by a **maximum** and **minimum** **thermometer**. During the day, the mercury or alcohol expands, pushing the metal pin higher on the scale. The opposite happens at night.

Fig. 1.2.1: **Maximum and minimum thermometers**

You may also come across digital thermometers for measuring maximum and minimum temperatures.

Rainfall is measured in mm by a **rain gauge**. It is sunk into the ground away from shelter; the rim must be 30 cm above the ground to avoid splashing. The water collected can be poured into a measuring jug and the level recorded.

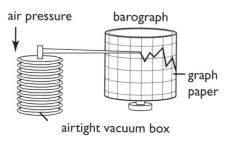

Fig. 1.2.2: **Rain gauge**

Air pressure is recorded on a **barograph** or **barometer**. As the weight of the air changes, the cylinder rises (or presses down) causing the lever to move and the pen to draw on the rotating drum.

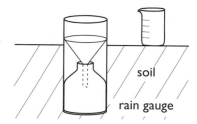

Fig. 1.2.3: **Barograph**

Wind is recorded by a **wind vane** which shows the direction from which the wind blows. An **anemometer** measures wind speed; a series of cups rotates as the wind speed increases. The velocity is measured in miles per hour or in knots. (A **wind meter** is also used.)

Fig. 1.2.4: **Wind vane and anemometer**

A Stevenson screen is a store where weather instruments are kept. It is white in order to reflect sunlight and slatted to allow air to circulate. It is placed above ground, on grass away from buildings and trees.

Fig. 1.2.5: Stevenson screen

Sample question

Try these sample questions for yourself. The answers are given at the back of the book.

Q. 1.1 Tick the correct answer.

(a) The local atmospheric conditions in a small area, such as school grounds, are called:
   (i)   weather
   (ii) precipitation
   (iii) microclimate.   (1)

(b) Air pressure in your local weather station is recorded using a
   (i)   thermometer
   (ii) barometer
   (iii) anemometer.   (1)

(c) Name three factors which may be very important in influencing the local climate (e.g. within the school grounds).   (3)

(d) Why might the local climate vary during the course of a bright, sunny day?   (4)

1.3 Rainfall types

Relief rainfall

(a) Evaporation causes warm, moist air to rise.

(b) Warm, moist air is forced up hill.

(c) Air cools and condenses, causing precipitation at dew point.

(d) Clouds form and rain falls.

(e) Air sinks over the other side of the hill; no rain falls here (rainshadow).

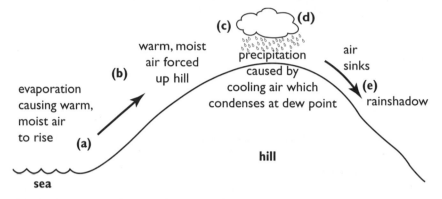

Fig. 1.3.1: Relief rainfall

Any hilly or mountainous place receives this rain, e.g. Wales, Scotland, the Alps and the Rockies.

Places at the foot of hills or mountains which do not face the prevailing wind are in the rainshadow and do not get very much rainfall.

Convectional rainfall

(a) Hot sun heats any water on the ground.

(b) Water from the ground is evaporated.

(c) Water vapour rises, cools and condenses at dew point.

(d) Clouds form and rain falls.

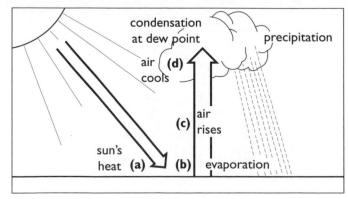

Fig. 1.3.2: Convectional rainfall

To receive convectional rainfall, a place must have strong sunshine and be relatively near a sea, lake or ocean, e.g. tropical rainforests.

Britain can experience convectional rain in the summer when it is very hot.

Tropical rainforests get convectional rain every day. The sun in the morning heats the puddles on the ground from the previous day's rain, then, by midday, it rains again.

Frontal rainfall

(a)   Warm air mass meets cold air mass.

(b)   Cold air is heavier, so undercuts warm air.

(c)   Warm air rises, cools and condenses at dew point.

(d)   Clouds form and it rains.

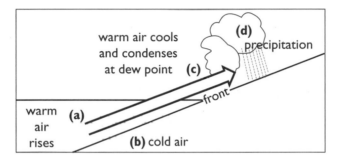

Fig. 1.3.3: Frontal rainfall

To receive frontal rain, a place needs air masses coming from tropical areas and polar areas.

Britain receives much frontal rain.

When hot air and cold air meet, air pressure is low, as air is rising. This weather system is called a depression and brings very changeable weather.

1.4 Factors affecting temperature

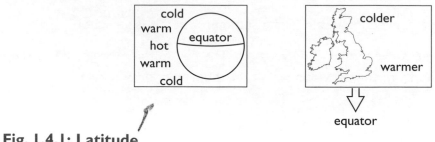

Fig. 1.4.1: Latitude

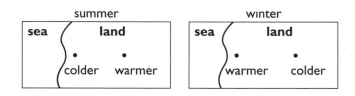

Fig. 1.4.2: Altitude

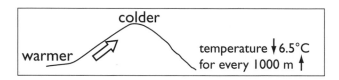

Fig. 1.4.3: Distance from the sea

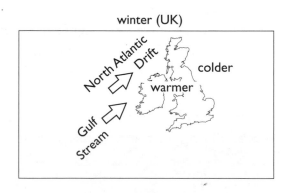

Fig. 1.4.4: Ocean currents

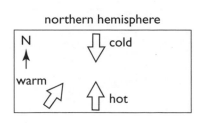

Fig. 1.4.5: Prevailing wind direction

1.5 Air pressure systems

Anticyclone	Depression
High air pressure Heavy air pushing down on the earth	**Low air pressure** Light air rising away from the earth
1. Air sinks	1. Warm air mass meets cool air mass
2. Air warms	2. Warm air rises over cool air to form a warm front
3. Clouds cannot be formed	3. Warm air rises along front, cools, condenses, clouds are formed
4. No precipitation	4. Precipitation occurs
Summer weather conditions Sun, light winds and high temperatures (heat wave)	**Summer weather conditions** Cloud, frontal precipitation and possibly strong winds
Winter weather conditions Sun, light winds, very low temperatures and frost	**Winter weather conditions** As above
N.B. Conditions remain for several days, or a week.	N.B. A depression can take a day to pass over, causing changeable weather.

1.6 A humid temperate climate (Britain)

North west

- mild summers (due to latitude)

- mild winters (due to ocean current)

- wet (due to relief and direction of prevailing wind)

North east

- mild summers (due to latitude)

- very cold winters (due to latitude)

- dry (as in rainshadow)

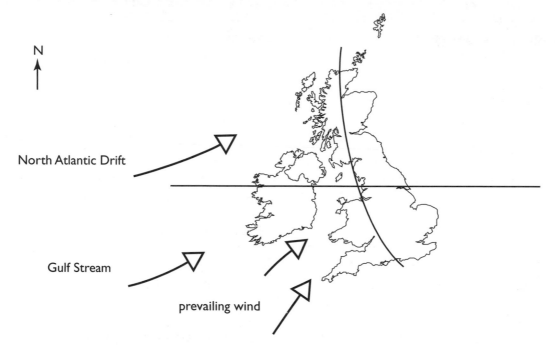

South west

- warm summers (due to latitude)

- mild winters (due to ocean current)

- wet (due to relief and direction of prevailing wind)

South east

- warm summers (due to latitude)

- cold winters (due to lack of effect of ocean current)

- dry (as in rainshadow)

Fig. 1.6.1: Britain's climate

1.7 A humid tropical climate

- **Location:** in equatorial regions: West Africa, South-East Asia, Northern Australia and South America, e.g. Amazonian rainforest in Brazil.

- **Rainfall:** over 2000 mm per annum.

- **Temperature:** 27°C (monthly average) – humid – not seasonal.

- **Vegetation:** layered; tall, straight-trunked trees; drip tips (spouts on leaves that channel water off the surface of the leaf); leaves with fronds.

Reasons for climate

- Sun overhead for most of year because of equatorial location – rays concentrated on small area causing high temperatures.

- Convectional rainfall as sunshine in the morning evaporates water, storm clouds form and heavy rainstorms occur in the afternoon.

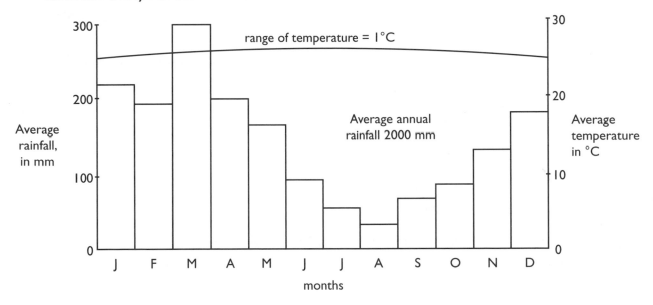

Sample question

Try these sample questions for yourself. The answers are given at the back of the book.

Q. 1.2 Describe how the climate in a humid tropical climate differs from that in a humid temperate climate. (3)

  1.3. Explain these differences. (3)

 Extra material is required here for pupils taking exams from Spring 2011 onwards. This is available to download from www.galorepark.co.uk

1.8 The water cycle (hydrological cycle)

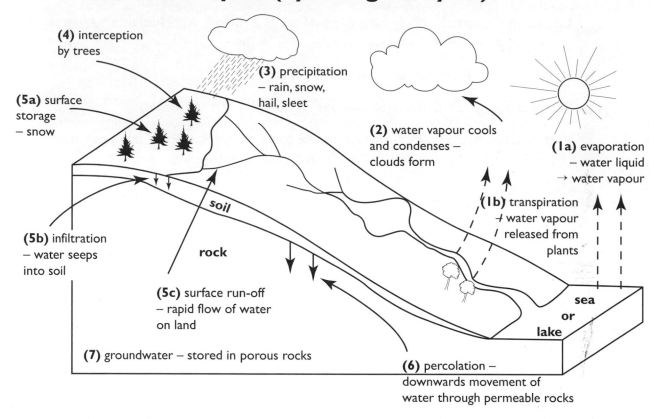

(4) interception by trees

(5a) surface storage – snow

(3) precipitation – rain, snow, hail, sleet

(2) water vapour cools and condenses – clouds form

(1a) evaporation – water liquid → water vapour

(1b) transpiration – water vapour released from plants

soil

(5b) infiltration – water seeps into soil

rock

(5c) surface run-off – rapid flow of water on land

sea or lake

(7) groundwater – stored in porous rocks

(6) percolation – downwards movement of water through permeable rocks

Fig. 1.8.1: The water cycle

2011

1.9 Weather/climate hazard

What are atmospheric hazards?

Tropical cyclones (hurricanes or typhoons or cyclones) usually occur in the tropics over warm oceans. Rising warm air causes towering clouds, heavy rainfall and intense low pressure. The low pressure sucks air in, causing very strong winds which spiral. They usually affect coastlines (deltas and islands are particularly at risk). They bring wind, rain and surge (an offshore rise in water) and occur due to low air pressure.

Tornadoes are a rotation of air, mainly in the USA (Tornado Alley) in spring but can also occur in the UK. They are short lasting and small (0.5 km wide and the path is usually 25 km long). The risk is the speed of the wind (60–100 km/h). They are formed when warm and cold air streams collide.

Hailstorms are created by ice crystals forming round atmospheric pollutants during intense storms whose up-draughts and down-draughts move the ice crystals up and down in the cloud, passing super-cooled water droplets which freeze around them. These are severe in the USA, particularly in Hail Alley, which stretches from the foothills of the Rockies to the Mississippi (daily damage between April and October). The heaviest hailstones ever recorded were in Bangladesh in 1986. They weighed over 1 kilogram each and killed 92 people.

Severe winter storms outside of the tropics often affect the UK (in 1987, 19 people died, in 1990, 46 people died and in January 2007, 11 people died). These are caused by erratic depressions (low air pressure) resulting in severe winds and heavy rain.

Snow and ice – snow can cause roofs or power lines to collapse, it can also cause avalanches and landslides. Ice can cause communication difficulties and treacherous roads. Snow forms when super-cooled water droplets and ice crystals exist together in a cloud causing the water droplet to condense on the ice crystal. The ice crystals collide and then fall, usually melting to form snow on their way down.

Fog occurs when visibility has decreased to less than 100 m. Severe disruption to transport occurs when visibility is down to 50 m. Fog is formed when the air is not able to hold all its water vapour invisibly. When air cools it is able to hold less water and becomes super-saturated. Some of this water therefore has to condense to form water droplets which create the fog. Fog is common on coastlines and in hilly areas.

Drought – in the UK a drought used to be defined as 15 consecutive days with less than 0.25 mm of rain. This led to problems, so now every organisation involved makes its own definition. 'Blocking' high pressure causes droughts as the high air pressure prevents air from rising and forming clouds and rain. UK droughts have occurred in summer 1976, the mid-80s and summer 2006. Parts of Africa are constantly suffering from drought and desertification (the land turning to desert). In 2006, East Africa (particularly Ethiopia, Somalia and Kenya) suffered. Ethiopia suffered an especially harsh drought in 1984.

Lightning is an electrical discharge from a cumulonimbus cloud. Lightning is five times hotter than the sun, so can destroy anything which it hits.

Case study 1.1 – Hurricane Katrina, August 2005

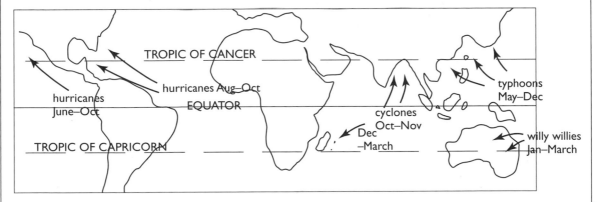

Fig. 1.9.1: Location of hurricane hazards in the world

Cause of Hurricane Katrina

- Formed when a cluster of thunderstorms drifted over the warm Caribbean Sea.

- The warm air from the ocean and the storm combined and rose – this created low pressure.

17

- Trade winds blowing in opposing directions and the Coriolis force caused the storm to spin.

- The rising warm air caused pressure to decrease at higher altitudes.

- The air rose faster and faster to fill this low pressure, drawing more warm air off the sea and sucking cooler, drier air downwards.

- The storm moved over the ocean and picked up more warm, moist air. Wind speeds started to pick up as more air was sucked into the low-pressure centre.

- There was an eye of calm winds surrounded by a spinning vortex of high winds and heavy rain.

- New Orleans is built in a bowl – the Mississippi had been controlled with levees and dams for years, and New Orleans was only in existence because of these. The city was suffering from subsidence as groundwater was extracted from underground and the coastline was disappearing. Louisiana has the highest rate of erosion in North America.

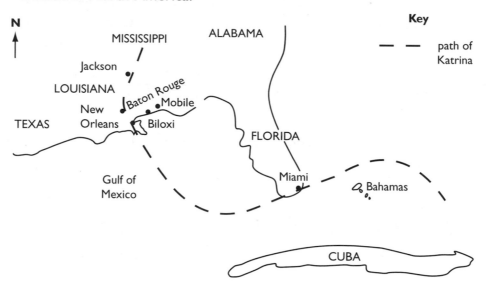

Fig. 1.9.2: Path of Hurricane Katrina

Nature of Hurricane Katrina

- Katrina hit the Florida coast on 25th August 2005, leaving 100 000 inhabitants without power.

- She veered inland towards Louisiana making landfall at Grand Isle (90 km south of New Orleans) – wind speed at this stage was 200 km/h on 29th August. She then hit New Orleans, Biloxi, Mobile and Jackson.

- Katrina was a Force 5 hurricane on the Saffir-Simpson scale (which means the wind speeds were faster than 249 km/h).

- Remember that Katrina was swiftly followed by Rita (Force 3) in September and then by Wilma in October.

Effects of Hurricane Katrina

Environmental

- Surge of 9 m in Biloxi covered land with water.

- Protective coastal mangroves were destroyed.

- The poorly maintained levees on the Mississippi broke, inundating New Orleans with flood water (80% of city inundated).

- Flood water and fires destroyed many buildings.

- Trees and vegetation were destroyed by flood.

- Fresh water was contaminated with salt water.

Social

- 1300 were killed, mainly in New Orleans.

- There were 500 000 refugees.

- The pollution of flood water with oil and snakes became a problem.

- Those who could not evacuate were left with a lack of water, food, power, fuel and communications, as they could not recharge their mobile phones.

- The disaster revealed the poverty of New Orleans, e.g. 50% of children were on welfare. Afro-American leaders became angry that this section of society was left behind.

- Poverty resulted in looting for food and the army's violent response came more quickly than aid.

- Many took refuge in the Superdome without proper sanitation or proper supplies; it became crowded and overheated.

Economic

- Work at oil refineries and platforms was halted.

- Casinos and businesses were looted.

- 400 000 homes and businesses were without power in Alabama.

- Huge blasts from a chemical plant rocked the city on 2nd September.

- Many left their businesses and have not returned, as they have been forced to start a new life elsewhere.

Human response to Hurricane Katrina

- 'Katrina was a national failure' (Congressional Report, February 2006).

- Aid was delayed by five days – Director of Federal Emergency Management Agency (FEMA) Michael Brown was dismissed from his post a week later.

- Evacuation drill consisted of saying 'leave town' – many could not speak English or could not afford to leave or were too ill to do this. Disaster drills did not consider the levee break.

- Bush had poor and incomplete advice, and a late decision to carry out a compulsory evacuation led to deaths and prolonged suffering.

- There was a lack of warning and no buses were provided for evacuation.

- FEMA suffered from a lack of trained and experienced personnel.

- Computer models predicted the levee failure, so the authorities should have been prepared.

- Helicopters dropped sandbags into the breach in the 17th Street Canal and earthmovers built a causeway allowing trucks to bring stones to repair levees.

- A temporary steel barrier was built at the mouth of the canal to seal it from Lake Pontchartrain.

- Areas were then pumped free of water.

- The impact of global warming causing sea levels to rise will make flooding an even greater threat in the future.

- Some believe that the chaos of Katrina has exposed deep divisions in New Orleans and US society. (Congressman Elijah Cummings said, 'We cannot allow it to be said by history that the difference between those who lived and … died … was nothing more than poverty, age or skin colour.')

- The congressional committee has spent months planning how to rebuild and revitalise housing, business and transport, and how levees and flood defences could be improved to prevent large-scale flooding in the future.

- Bush has promised $3.1 billion towards repairs and improvements over the next few years.

- The US Army Corps plan to have temporary repairs in place for the next hurricane season.

- The Red Cross served 995 000 meals in one day alone.

- The Mississippi River Gulf Outlet, built in the 1960s, allowed ships easy access to the Gulf of Mexico via the Port of New Orleans. However, the channel has increased from 91 m to 914 m wide due to deliberate widening and natural action. The storm surge of Katrina passed up this channel. Plans to close it altogether are being considered.

- The congressional report divides the city of New Orleans into three zones:

  - Immediate Opportunity Areas with little damage;

  - Neighbourhood Planning Areas with severely damaged properties;

  - Infill Development Zone where private and public land with run-down properties on high land can be developed for housing and commercial use.

Case study notes

Use this page to make notes on what you have learned about the hurricane case study.

Perhaps draw a box and bubble flow chart to help you revise. For help with these see *Study Skills* by Elizabeth Holtom, published by Galore Park.

> **Sample question**
>
> Try this sample question for yourself. A suggested answer is given at the back of the book.
>
> **Q.** 1.4 For an extreme weather event which you have studied, explain why it occurred. (6)

Summary

You should now know the following:

1. The factors affecting microclimates.

2. The different instruments used to measure weather.

3. The different types of rainfall.

4. The different factors affecting temperature.

5. *How air pressure systems work.*

6. The key features of the humid temperate climate of Britain.

7. The key features of a humid tropical climate.

8. *What causes the water cycle.*

9. *The key features of weather/climate hazards.*

10. *The details of your chosen case study.*

Remember: only items in *italics* will not be examined from Spring 2011. All items will be examined until Summer 2010.

2011

2011

Test yourself

Before moving on to the next chapter, make sure you can answer the following questions. The answers to questions 1–3 are at the back of the book.

2011

1. (a) *What is the name given to a low air pressure system?*

   (b) *What weather conditions does it bring?*

2. (a) *What is the name given to a high air pressure system?*

   (b) *What weather conditions does it bring?*

3. Write out each of these sentences using the correct word or words to finish the sentence:

   (a) Rain, hail, snow and sleet are all forms of
      infiltration   precipitation   rainfall   weather system

   (b) The prevailing wind direction for the UK is from the
      south-east   north-west   south-west   north-east

   (c) The Gulf Stream is
      an ocean current   a wind   a river   an island

   (d) The Gulf Stream and North Atlantic Drift affect the south-west of the UK
      in summer   all the year round   in spring   in winter

   (e) Moist air forced to rise over upland areas causes
      relief rainfall   frontal rainfall   convectional rainfall

4. Fill in this glossary list in pencil and ask your teacher to check you have filled it in correctly.

   air mass . . . .

   air pressure . . . .

   altitude . . . .

   anemometer . . . .

2011

   anticyclone . . . .

   aspect . . . .

   atmosphere . . . .

   barograph (barometer) . . . .

   climate . . . .

climate graph ....

condensation ....

convectional rainfall ....

depression ....

desert ....

dew point ....

drought ....

equator ....

evaporation ....

fog ....

front ....

frontal rainfall ....

ground water ....

Gulf Stream ....

humid temperate climate ....

humid tropical climate ....

humidity ....

infiltration ....

interception ....

isobars ....

isotherm ....

latitude ....

maximum thermometer ....

microclimate ....

minimum thermometer ....

North Atlantic Drift ....

percolation ....

precipitation ....

prevailing wind ....

rain gauge ....

rain shadow ....

relief rainfall ....

seasonal ....

shelter ....

Stevenson screen ....

surface run-off ....

throughflow ....

transpiration ....

water cycle ....

weather ....

wind vane ....

Chapter 2: Geomorphology

2.1 Types of weathering

- **Weathering** – the breaking down of rocks by weather, plants and animals.
- **Erosion** – the wearing away and removal of rocks by rivers, sea, ice and wind.

Physical weathering

Freeze-thaw weathering

- Water seeps into crack.
- Water freezes.
- Ice expands.
- Crack is forced open.
- Process is repeated.
- Rock breaks up (loose rock known as scree).

Freeze-thaw is common in mountainous areas. Igneous rocks (granite) and metamorphic rocks (marble) from uplands are prone to this type of weathering.

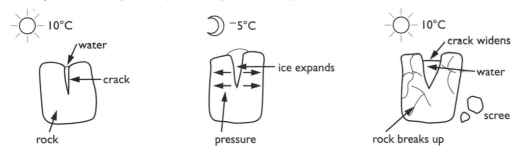

Fig. 2.1.1: Freeze-thaw weathering

Onion-skin weathering or exfoliation

- Rock is repeatedly subjected to heat and cold.
- Outer layer expands in heat.
- Outer layer contracts in cold.
- Outer layer of rock peels off (loose rock known as scree).

This type of weathering is common in desert areas which are hot in the day and cool at night.

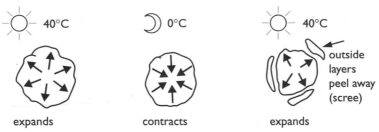

Fig. 2.1.2: Onion-skin weathering

Biological weathering

- Burrowing animals break up rocks.
- Plant seeds fall in cracks and grow into trees; roots exert pressure on crack causing it to widen.

Chemical weathering

- Rain contains carbonic acid.
- Acid attacks rock.
- Rock crumbles.

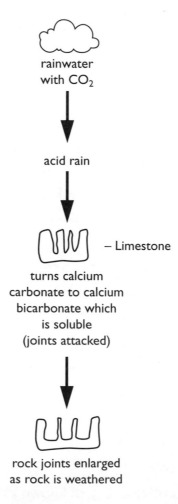

rainwater
with CO_2

acid rain

— Limestone

turns calcium
carbonate to calcium
bicarbonate which
is soluble
(joints attacked)

rock joints enlarged
as rock is weathered

Fig. 2.1.3: Chemical weathering

Sedimentary rocks, such as limestone and chalk, are particularly vulnerable to this type of weathering; limestone gravestones are commonly attacked.

Limestone pavements are also vulnerable as the acid water can seep into the grykes (deep cracks) and attack a large surface area. As the carbonic acid falls on limestone, it turns it into calcium bicarbonate which is soluble in water.

2.2 Rock types

Igneous

This is formed from volcanic rock. If the magma has cooled underground, granite is formed. If it reaches the Earth's surface, it is called lava which forms basalt when it cools.

Sedimentary

This is formed when rivers have transported particles of rock and remains of plants and animals to the sea which have sunk to the sea bed and, over millions of years, compressed to form new rock.

Metamorphic

This is formed from sedimentary or igneous rock when exposed to extreme pressure or heat during the Earth's movements, e.g. chalk and limestone turn to marble; clay turns to slate.

2.3 The drainage basin of a river

- **Drainage basin** of a river – the area of land drained by a river and its tributaries.

- **Watershed** – the edge of the drainage basin.

- **Source** – start of the river.

- **Tributary** – small stream or river running into the main river channel.

- **Confluence** – where the tributary meets up with the main channel.

- **Meander** – bend in the river.

- **Ox-bow lake** – where a meander is cut off to form a small lake.

- **Flood plain** – flat land in the lower course of the river which is prone to flooding.

- **Mouth** – where the river reaches the sea (sometimes forming a delta).

- **Estuary** – where sea (salt) water mixes with fresh water, forming brackish water, and a widened mouth occurs.

- **Delta** – where the river channel splits into distributaries as the river dumps the remainder of its load as it meets salt water.

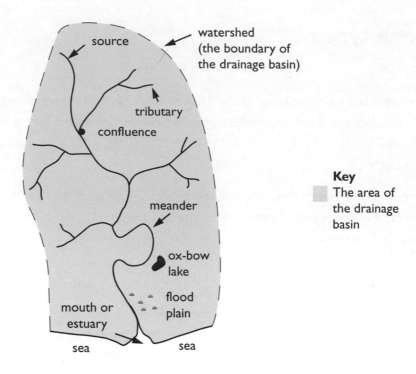

Fig. 2.3.1: River drainage basin

2.4 River processes

River erosion

As the river channel moves through the drainage basin, it alters the landscape due to the wearing away and removal of land caused by the following processes:

- **Attrition** – particles of load colliding and knocking pieces off each other.

- **Abrasion** – smaller material rubbing against the bed and banks.

- **Corrosion** – acid in water dissolving the bed and banks.

- **Hydraulic action** – sheer force of the water and air forcing into soil and moving away parts of the bed and banks.

Transportation

Once the material (known as load) has been eroded, it is then carried along the river by the following processes:

- **Traction** – stones rolling along the bed.

- **Saltation** – particles 'leap-frogging' along the bed.

- **Suspension** – material carried within the water flow.

- **Solution** – material dissolved in water.

Deposition

When the river slows down, the load is 'dumped'. This is known as deposition. Large boulders are deposited first and fine sediment last.

2.5 Features of the upper course

V-shaped valley

This is a feature of erosion. It occurs when the river erodes downwards into the land by abrasion and hydraulic action. This is called **vertical erosion**. The valley sides are then shaped by the weather, plants and animals (weathering).

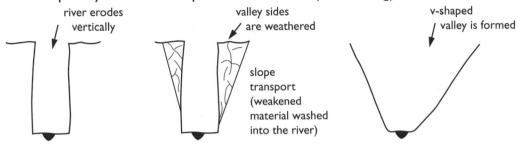

Fig. 2.5.1: V-shaped valley formation

Waterfall

This is a feature of erosion. It occurs when a river flowing over hard rock meets a band of softer, less resistant rock.

Hydraulic action and abrasion erode the softer rock forming a 'step' in the river bed.

The softer rock is undercut and the hard rock is left as overhang. A plunge pool is formed at the base of the waterfall; this plunge pool is deepened by abrasion as the pebbles erode its base.

The overhang eventually collapses and in this way the waterfall retreats towards the source of the river, forming a gorge.

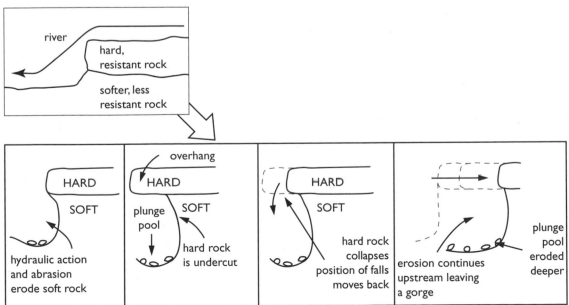

Fig. 2.5.2: Waterfall formation

2.6 Features of the lower course

Meanders

This is a feature of erosion and deposition. The river is dynamic – it is constantly changing its shape and therefore has a lot of meanders (bends) in it. These meanders are formed by **lateral** (sideways) **erosion**.

Ⓐ : Outside of a meander	Ⓑ : Inside of a meander
river cliff fast velocity erosion (hydraulic action and abrasion) deeper water	river beach / slip-off slope slow velocity deposition shallow water

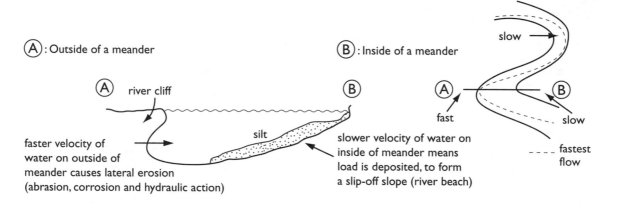

Fig. 2.6.1: Meanders

Ox-bow lake

This is a feature of erosion and deposition. It occurs where the horseshoe-shaped meander becomes tighter, until the ends become very close together and join to form a separate lake.

The outside of two meanders are eroded by **hydraulic action** and **abrasion**.

The river becomes more **sinuous** (has more curves and turns).

This results in a narrow neck of land remaining between the two river cliffs.

Eventually, perhaps during a flood, the narrow neck of land is eroded away and the water takes the more direct straight route downstream.

Deposition occurs and eventually the old meander loop is separated from the river and forms an ox-bow lake.

Evaporation will usually cause the lake to become dry eventually.

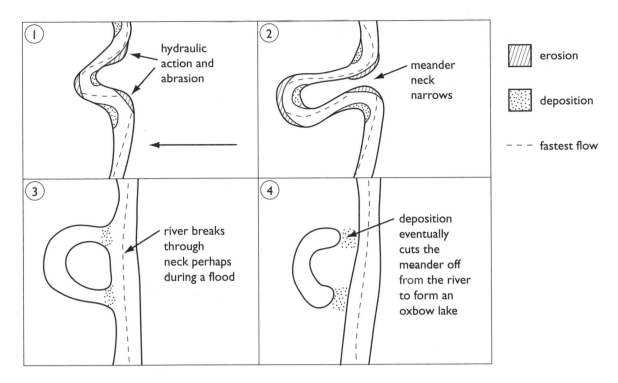

Fig. 2.6.2: Oxbow lake formation

Deltas

This is a feature of deposition (e.g. the Nile Delta / the Mississippi Delta). As large rivers approach the sea, they carry a large amount of **load** (material) in suspension.

The speed (velocity) of the river is reduced as it reaches the more powerful sea, so it has less energy and deposits its load to form new land.

The coarser material is deposited first and then the finer material.

With time, more and more sand and silt is deposited.

The river divides into channels called **distributaries** which flow round the deposits of new land.

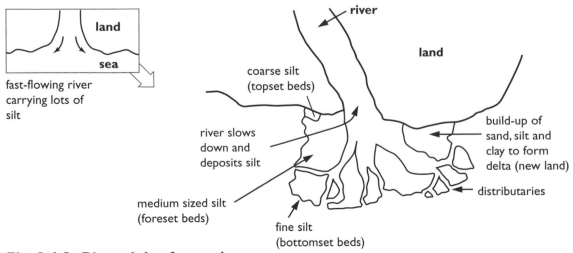

Fig. 2.6.3: River delta formation

Flood plain

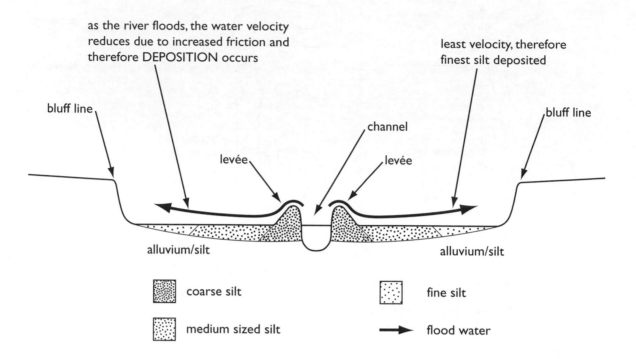

Fig. 2.6.4: Flood plain

This is a feature of deposition. It occurs when a river floods and deposits its load.

As the water spills out of its channel, friction increases as the water flows over the land at the side of the channel.

The larger pieces of load are deposited first, often forming natural **levees** near the channel, and the finer sediment is transported further.

The flat land onto which flood water flows is known as the **flood plain**.

Sample question

Try these sample questions for yourself. Suggested answers are given at the back of the book.

Q. 2.1 Hydraulic action is one type of river erosion.
    (i) Name another river erosion process. (1)
    (ii) Describe how this process works. (3)

    2.2 What do you call the material transported in a river? (1)

    2.3 How does the size and shape of the material transported in a river change from source to mouth? (3)

2.7 Reasons for and effects of river floods

Reasons

Climatic reasons

- Heavy rainfall over a short or long period of time.
- Ground saturated from previous rainfall.
- Melting snow and glaciers.

Physical reasons

- Narrow steep-sided valley causing surface run-off to reach river rapidly after storm.
- Small drainage basin causing rapid surface run-off.
- Impermeable rock causing rapid surface run-off.

Human reasons

- Urbanisation leading to increase in tarmac and drains causing rapid surface run-off.
- Deforestation in drainage basin leading to less water taken up by roots.
- Diversion of river or narrowing of channel.
- Silting due to deforestation.

Effects

- Buildings washed away or damaged.
- People and animals drowned.
- Communications damaged due to closed roads and impassable railways.
- Crops ruined (agricultural economy suffers).
- Insurance claimed.
- Drinking water contaminated by sewage, leading to disease.
- Beneficial effect – silt deposited, providing fertile soil for farming.

Flood control

- Construction of dams to control discharge.
- Construction of levees and dykes to contain water.
- Straightening of meanders to remove flood water quickly.
- Afforestation to increase transpiration and infiltration.
- Sandbagging to prevent flooding of buildings.

Example 2.1 – Boscastle floods, 16th August 2004

Flash floods occurred in the valleys of the River Valency and the River Jordan.

Physical causes

Topographical

- Narrow valley with interlocking spurs which acted like a funnel.
- Steep valley which encouraged rapid run-off.
- Village of Boscastle is situated on a flat flood plain.
- Soil type in the area is impermeable clay which did not allow much infiltration.

Climatic

- 185 mm of rain fell in five hours.
- The soil was saturated from recent rainfall so no more rain could infiltrate.
- There was a collision of winds on a very warm day. (The air mass from the south met the air mass from the south-west and converged on Bodmin which led to towering cumulonimbus clouds. The air was very unstable and the clouds were up to 10 km high.)

Human causes

- The natural channel had been walled (for the construction of the B3263 and a pedestrian area) which prevented it from adjusting to variation in discharge.
- The village had been built on a flat flood plain.
- There was a lack of any flood control system.
- Cars, trees and boulders became stuck under the bridge which caused a temporary dam causing the water to build up behind it.
- The sewers and drainage systems were old and small in capacity; they broke and this water took an overland route.

Effects

- Fifty cars were swept into the harbour.
- The bridge was washed away and roads were submerged under 2.75 m of water, making communication difficult.
- The sewerage system burst.
- Due to health and safety reasons Boscastle was declared inaccessible.
- The Museum of Witchcraft lost 50% of its artefacts.

- Four buildings were demolished and 58 flooded and the High Street was badly damaged.

- Clovelly Clothing, the visitors' centre and two gift shops were badly damaged.

- The youth hostel was flooded.

- People were in shock and there was concern about hypothermia or being swept away.

- There was no power in the village. (An emergency generator had to be flown in.)

- 90% of the economy is based on tourism and there were still three weeks of the summer holidays left; twenty accommodation providers were shut.

- Tourists who had arrived during the day could not return if their cars had been washed away.

Responses

- A speedy, well-coordinated and well-resourced rescue operation ensured that remarkably there was no loss of life. Even by more economically developed countries (MEDC) standards this was outstanding and a tribute to Britain's rescue services.

- Emergency workers rescued residents and holiday-makers from a 32 km stretch of the north Cornwall coast.

- Hundreds were evacuated from homes, rooftops (120 from rooftops), trees and vehicles.

- Seven helicopters from the Coastguards, Royal Navy and RAF were used.

- People took emergency shelter in The Rectory which was on high ground.

- People came to see the catastrophe, despite the 'no entry' signs.

- Prince Charles and John Prescott came to see the damage.

- The clean-up operation started and the village was cordoned off by the building inspectors.

- There was a church service to give thanks that no one had died.

- People dug out guttering and removed rubble so that the water could flow away.

- Sandbagging was used as a form of defence.

- The repairs were very costly and time consuming.

- There was a huge fund-raising effort to help rebuild.

- Insurance is now costlier in Boscastle.

Flood prevention

- The Environment Agency carried out a major investigation.

- £2 million grant was given to Boscastle to help with flood prevention.

- No more schools or old people's homes are to be built in the valley.

- The Environment Agency removed debris from upstream, which meant more room for the water to flow freely under the new bridge.

- However, flood barriers have not been built.

- There was a plan for a flood defence system (flood wall, widening river, raising car parks, removal of bridges and using relief channels) on the River Jordan but this was postponed, as it was thought it would affect the tourist trade.

Example 2.2 – Flooding in Bangladesh, 1998

Floods occur each year in Bangladesh. The majority of Bangladesh's 140 million inhabitants live on the floodplains of the Ganges and Brahmaputra and they need the floods to grow rice and jute. Also the floods deposit silt which they need to make the soil fertile. However, often the inundation (flooding) is so intense that lives and crops are ruined. Bangladesh suffers from two types of flood: river flooding and storm surges (coastal flooding) from the Bay of Bengal.

Bangladesh can get more rain in four months than London gets in two years!

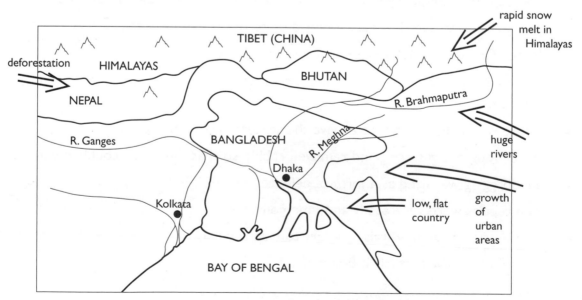

Fig. 2.7.1: Location and causes of the flood in Bangladesh

Physical causes

- Half the country lies less than 6 metres above sea level.

- Most of the population live on the silt deposited by the Ganges and the Brahmaputra Rivers which forms a delta. However the continuous deposition of silt tends to block the main channels and raise the heights of river beds, making severe floods more likely.

- Once rivers overflow their banks, the water can spread a vast distance on the flat delta floodplain.

- Bangladesh has a monsoon climate receiving between 1800 mm and 2600 mm of rainfall per year. However, 80% of this rainfall takes place in four months (June to September). In 1998 rainfall was so intense that there were three peaks of high rainfall in July, August and September (this last peak was unusually late).

- There are high temperatures from June to September which means that ice and snow melt in the Himalayas, where the Ganges and Brahmaputra have their sources and tributaries.

- The flood water was above danger level for 67 days from June to September.

- Tropical cyclones which are funnelled up the Bay of Bengal make sea levels rise and stop the river flood water escaping. As the land becomes shallower, the water builds up to form a surge up to 6 metres in height.

- High tides in the Bay of Bengal stop the flood water being able to escape.

Human causes

- Global warming is causing glaciers in the Himalayas to melt and the sea level of the Bay of Bengal to rise.

- Urbanisation on the floodplains (delta) has led to more run-off and a shorter lag time.

- Deforestation in the upper course of the river (Nepal) has led to more run-off which allows more sediment to build up, which leads to higher risk of flooding.

- Extraction of ground water for irrigation has lowered the water table and caused the land to subside by about 2.5 metres.

- Farming on the slopes has caused much soil erosion, which in turn causes silting of rivers which can lead to flooding.

Effects on the land

- In July 30% of the country was under water, in August 40% and in September 70%. The optimum amount of flooding to aid agriculture is 20%.

- Some places were flooded for more than 70 days.

- The flood was so deep in places that only the tops of roofs and trees could be seen.

- Large areas of Dhaka (capital city) were flooded, particularly the eastern area (the western area was protected by an embankment).

- 'Char' areas (low flat land made up of deposited silt) were destroyed.

- The deposits left by this severe flood were infertile sand rather than silt. When the water receded the land was infertile.

- The devastation was great, as in a less economically developed country (LEDC) many are too poor to own a telephone or TV and did not get advance warning to escape.

Effects on the people

- 700 000 hectares of crops were damaged or destroyed – this led to food shortages.

- At least 2379 people were killed.

- 130 million cattle died, leading to food shortages.

- Infrastructure such as roads, railways and bridges (6500) were destroyed, causing 11 000 kilometres of roads to be closed.

- 7 million homes were destroyed and 25 million people were made homeless.

- Most parts of the country were without electricity for several weeks.

- Flood water had polluted wells so there was no safe drinking water.

- As people evacuated to higher ground, crowding caused the spread of dysentery, cholera and diarrhoea.

- Hospitals were full.

- 1000 schools were damaged.

- People ran out of money to buy food and could not work as the land was submerged.

- Dhaka International Airport was under 2 metres of water.

Responses

- 1 million tons of food grain was imported.

- Medical care and water purification tablets were provided in treatment centres and by mobile teams.

- Concrete flood shelters on stilts were built in low-lying agricultural areas.

- Newspapers gave advice on how to avoid drinking dirty water.

- The poorest were identified by Save the Children Fund and Oxfam and given food assistance.

- Vitamin A capsules were distributed.

- People took out loans during or after the flood from Mohajons (moneylenders who charge very high interest rates, e.g. 200% per year). Some sold any remaining possessions which they had.

- After the bad flooding that occurred in 1988, the Flood Action Plan (costing over $650 million) was proposed by rich countries to be funded by the World Bank. The plan included the construction of large embankments to protect major cities, roads, rail and agricultural land. The country lacked the technology and money for impressive schemes such as the Thames Flood Barrier.

- There has been criticism of this plan, as to whether it is sustainable, as it narrows the flood plain and increases the height of rivers, depriving many areas of fish and fertile silt. It would also be very expensive.

- Appropriate technology has been suggested as an alternative. This would allow flooding but hopefully control extreme flooding. The Appropriate Technology Plan includes improving early warning systems, by the distribution of leaflets and enlisting 33 000 volunteers to educate people on preparing and coping with future floods.

- The 1988 flood only lasted a third of the time of the 1998 flood but killed twice as many people, indicating that forecasting and earlier deliveries of aid and the Flood Action Plan had some effect.

Case study notes

Use this page to make notes on what you have learned about the flood case studies.

Perhaps draw a box and bubble flow chart to help you revise. For help with these see *Study Skills* by Elizabeth Holtom, published by Galore Park.

2.8 Coastal erosion

Coastal erosion is caused by:

- **Hydraulic action** – water trapping air in cracks and caves and the force of the water itself against the cliffs.

- **Corrosion** – dissolving of rock by acid in water.

- **Attrition** – pebbles hitting each other in the waves.

- **Abrasion** – waves throwing pebbles at cliffs.

Features of erosion are:

- Headlands and bays.

- Caves, arches, stacks and stumps.

Headlands and bays

These are features of erosion and deposition.

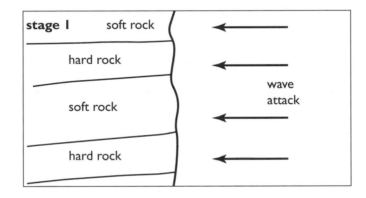

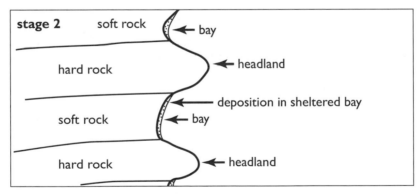

Fig. 2.8.1: Headland and bay formation on discordant coastline

A geographer's recipe for bay and headland formation

Ingredients:

- Alternating hard and soft rock (discordant coastline).

- Wave attack.

Caves, arches, stacks and stumps

These are features of erosion (see Fig. 2.8.2 opposite).

- Waves attack fault by hydraulic action and abrasion ①.

- Fault is enlarged to form a cave ②.

- Cave is widened and deepened by hydraulic action and abrasion which cuts through a headland to form an arch ③.

- Undercutting, weathering and lack of support for the arch leads to collapse, leaving a stack ④.

- Weathering and erosion turns the stack into a stump ⑤.

- A wave cut platform could be formed as the cliff retreats through erosion by waves; a platform of rock is left extending into the sea.

(See Fig 2.8.2 opposite)

Sample question

Try this sample question for yourself. The answer is given at the back of the book.

Q. 2.4 Describe the processes involved in the erosion of a headland. (5)

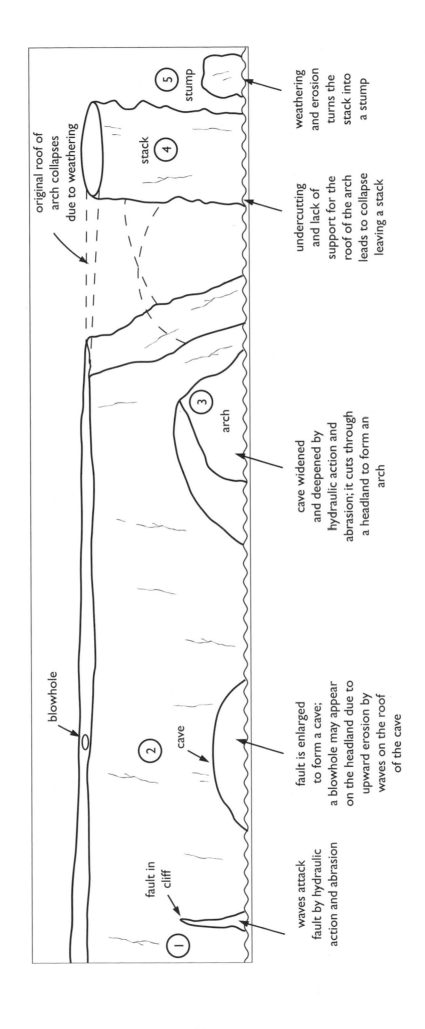

Fig. 2.8.2: Cave, arch, stack and stump formation

waves attack fault by hydraulic action and abrasion

fault in cliff

①

fault is enlarged to form a cave; a blowhole may appear on the headland due to upward erosion by waves on the roof of the cave

blowhole

cave

②

cave widened and deepened by hydraulic action and abrasion; it cuts through a headland to form an arch

arch

③

original roof of arch collapses due to weathering

undercutting and lack of support for the roof of the arch leads to collapse leaving a stack

stack

④

weathering and erosion turns the stack into a stump

stump

⑤

2.9 Coastal transportation

Longshore drift – the movement of sediment along the beach by waves.

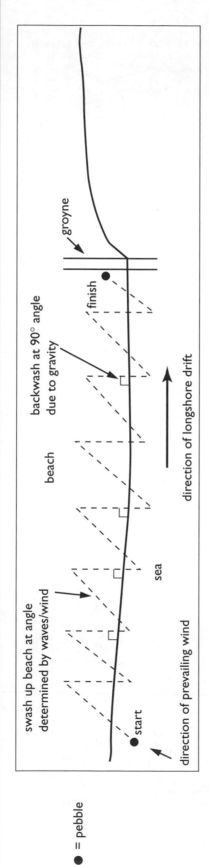

Fig. 2.9.1: Coastal transportation

2.10 Coastal deposition

Beaches and spits (e.g. Hurst Castle Spit, Hampshire) are features of deposition.

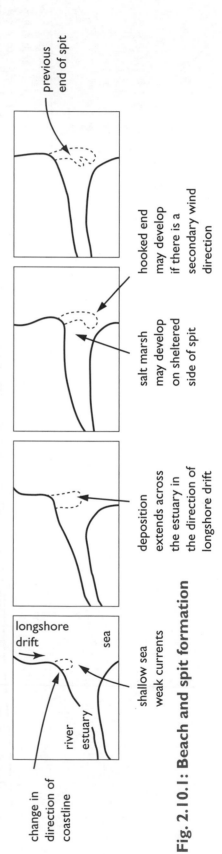

Fig. 2.10.1: Beach and spit formation

A geographer's recipe for spit formation

Ingredients:

- Weak currents.
- Shallow water.
- A change in direction of coastline.
- Occurrence of longshore drift.

Sample question

Try this sample question for yourself. The answer is given at the back of the book.

Q. 2.5 Describe and draw the processes involved in the formation of a spit. (5)

2.11 Landslides

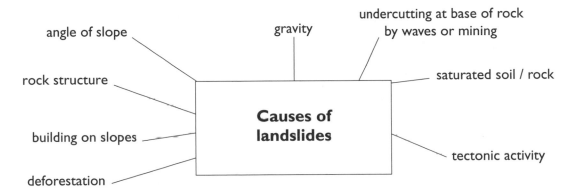

Fig. 2.11.1: Causes of landslides

Example 2.3 – Aberfan (Wales, 1966)

Causes

- Unstable (too steep / loose rock) spoil heap situated only 250 m away from village.

- Saturated rock due to heavy rain.

- Base of rock eroded by a spring, causing heap to collapse.

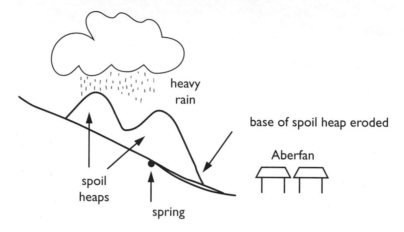

Fig. 2.11.2: Causes of Aberfan spoil heap collapse

Effects

- 2 million tonnes of rock flowed to village.

- Twenty houses were destroyed.

- 116 children and 28 adults were killed (mainly in a primary school).

- One farm was destroyed.

Results

- National Coal Board paid compensation.

- Strict regulations now ensure heaps are safe.

Example 2.4 – Llipi (Bolivia, 1992)

Causes

- Farmers trying to become rich by gold mining, creating steep quarry sides.

- Unregulated mining, safety ignored.

- Heavy rainfall causing saturated soil.

- Deforestation.

Effects

- 1200 people were killed.

2.12 Glaciation

Much scenery in Britain owes its beauty to glaciers. Northern Britain was covered in an ice sheet in the ice age and glaciers extended down valleys.

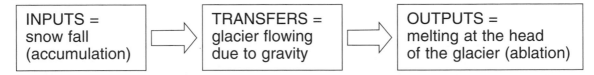

Fig. 2.12.1: The glacier as a system

If accumulation is greater than ablation the glacier will advance. If ablation is greater than accumulation the glacier will retreat.

Processes of erosion

- A glacier gains material from the valley side and floor through the process of freeze-thaw weathering.

- The glacier uses this material (moraine) to widen and deepen its valley through erosion.

- There are two main types of glacial erosion:

  Abrasion – moraine frozen in the glacier is rubbed like sandpaper along the valley floor and sides, wearing them away and leaving scratch marks called striations.

  Plucking – glacial ice freezes onto solid rock and as the glacier moves it pulls with it the pieces of rock.

Processes of transportation

- Moraine is transported frozen into the glacier.

- Moraine is deposited when there is a rise of temperature and the glacier melts.

Features of deposition in a glacial landscape

(see Fig. 2.12.2 on page 50)

- **Lateral moraine** is carried at the sides of the glacier and is formed from freeze-thaw action on the valley sides.

- **Medial moraine** is found in the centre of the glacier when the inside lateral moraines of two glaciers merge together.

- **Ground moraine** (till or boulder clay) is material dragged under the glacier, which when deposited forms the flat valley floor.

- **Terminal moraine** marks the maximum advance of the glacier or the snout of the glacier.

- **Recessional moraines** are behind the terminal moraine and mark positions where the glacier remained stationary for a while.

- **Erratic** is a piece of rock or boulder that the glacier has carried which has been deposited in an area of totally different rock.

- **Drumlins** are smooth, elongated mounds of material deposited when they become too heavy. These deposits have been smoothed by later ice movement.

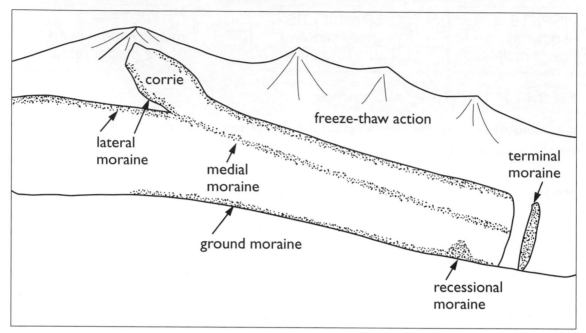

Fig. 2.12.2: Features of deposition in a glacial environment

Features of erosion in a glacial landscape

Corrie (cirque or cwm) (see Fig. 2.12.3 on page 51)

- These are formed at the beginning of an ice age when snow accumulates in hollows on hill sides ①.

- The snow turns to ice and the ice moves downhill.

- Freeze-thaw and plucking loosens and removes material from the back wall creating a steep wall ②.

- Moraine is dragged along the base deepening the floor and forming a rock basin ②.

- A rock lip is left where the rate of erosion has decreased, heightened by moraine deposition ③.

- This often acts as a natural dam to melt water after the ice age.

- The saucer-shaped depression also fills with rainwater forming a corrie lake for as long as the dam / lip remains intact (often thousands of years after the ice disappeared).

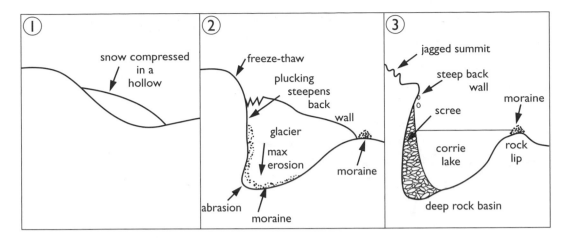

Fig. 2.12.3: Formation of a corrie

Arête and pyramidal peak (see Fig. 2.12.4 on page 52)

- Arêtes form when two or more corries develop back to back or side by side.

- The land between them gets narrower until a knife-edge ridge is formed called an arête.

- When three or more corries retreat backwards on each other a pyramidal peak or horn develops, e.g. the Matterhorn in Switzerland.

Glacial trough (see Fig. 2.12.4 on page 52)

- V-shaped valleys are eroded into U-shaped valleys known as glacial troughs.

- Interlocking spurs are eroded away and the valley is deepened and straightened.

Truncated spur (see Fig. 2.12.4 on page 52)

- As the glacier erodes a glacial trough, it carves off the spurs which reach into the valley.

Hanging valley (see Fig. 2.12.4 on page 52)

- The glaciers in the tributary valleys of the main valley are much smaller and thus less erosive.

- Therefore, when the glacier melts, the tributary valleys are left hanging above the main valley and the rivers which then flow into them meet the main valley with a waterfall.

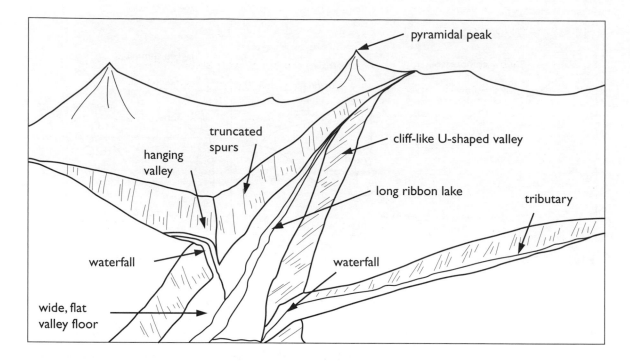

Fig. 2.12.4: Glacial troughs, truncated spurs and hanging valleys

Summary

You should now know the following:

1.   The different types of weathering.

2.   The different rock types.

3.   The features of a drainage basin of a river.

4.   The different river processes.

5.   The features of the upper and lower courses of a river.

6.   The reasons why rivers flood and the effects of flooding.

7.   The features and causes of coastal erosion.

8.   The main features of coastal transportation and deposition.

9.   The main features and causes of landslides.

10. *The main features of glaciation.*

Test yourself

Before moving on to the next chapter, make sure you can answer the following questions. The answers to questions 1–6 are at the back of the book.

1. Using the words given below, write out the following paragraphs filling in the gaps.

   transports   outside   speed   inside   reduces

   river   cliff   increases   river beach   slip-off slope   delta

   Velocity is the .... of the water. Deposition is the 'dumping' of a load when the river's velocity .... Load is the material which the river .... Load can be deposited by rivers at their mouth; the feature formed is called a .... It is also deposited on the .... bend of a meander; the feature formed is called a ....

2. Copy and complete the table to show how the shape and size of a river's load changes from upper course to lower course.

	Upper course	Lower course
Size of load		
Shape of load		
Main methods of transportation		

3. To which type of weathering will the following be most prone?
   (a) Rocks in a tropical rain forest.
   (b) Mountainous areas.
   (c) Rocks in a desert.

4. Match heads to tails! (The first one is done for you.) Note you will have come across some of these terms in Chapter 1.

Drainage basin	the movement of water over the surface of the land back to the sea
Watershed	rocks which allow water to pass through them
Source	when the river's load collides and breaks into smaller pieces
Mouth	the downwards movement of water through tiny pores in the soil
Permeable	the movement of water through the soil back to the sea
Impermeable	the loss of moisture to the air from plants
Evaporation	the amount of water which passes a given point at a given time, measured in cumecs (cubic metres per second)
Transpiration	an area of land drained by a river and its tributaries
Through flow	the start of a river
Ground water storage	where the river meets the sea
Infiltration	water stored in rocks below the ground
Surface run-off	the material which a river carries
River discharge	a type of erosion where the force of the water breaks particles of rock from the river bank
Load	rock which does not allow water to pass through
Attrition	the loss of water to the air when the water has turned into water vapour
Corrosion	a type of erosion when the acids in the river dissolve the rocks
Hydraulic action	the boundary of the drainage basin, usually marked by a ridge of high land

5. Tick the correct answer.

(a) Which of the following is a process where rocks in the ice grind against the rock over which the ice is flowing?

- abrasion
- plucking
- freeze-thaw
- corrosion

(b) When the ice melts, it leaves these steep-sided hollows often with lakes in them.

- hanging valleys
- roches moutonnées
- corries
- truncated spurs

(c) This type of deposit shows the furthest point reached by the glacier. What is this called?

- lateral moraine
- medial moraine
- erratic
- terminal moraine

6.

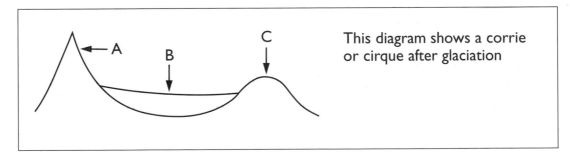

This diagram shows a corrie or cirque after glaciation

(a) What are features:

A ....

B ....

C ....

(b) Describe how an arête is formed.

7. Fill in this glossary list in pencil and ask your teacher to check you have filled it in correctly.

ablation . . . .

abrasion . . . .

accumulation . . . .

arch . . . .

arête . . . .

attrition . . . .

bay . . . .

beach . . . .

bedding plane . . . .

biological weathering . . . .

cave . . . .

chemical weathering . . . .

confluence . . . .

corrie (cirque or cwm) . . . .

corrosion . . . .

dam . . . .

delta . . . .

deposition . . . .

drainage basin . . . .

drumlin . . . .

dyke . . . .

erosion . . . .

2011

2011

2011

erratic . . . .   `2011`

estuary . . . .

fault . . . .

fetch . . . .

flood plain . . . .

freeze-thaw weathering . . . .

glacier . . . .   `2011`

glacier trough . . . .

gorge . . . . ,,,,

hanging valley . . . .   `2011`

headland . . . .

hydraulic action . . . .

hydro-electric power . . . .

igneous rock . . . .

impermeable . . . .

interlocking spurs . . . .

joint . . . .   `2011`

landslide . . . .

levee . . . .

limestone . . . .

load . . . .

longshore drift . . . .

mass movement . . . .

meander . . . .

metamorphic rock . . . .

moraine . . . .

mouth . . . .

onion-skin weathering (exfoliation) . . . .

ox-bow lake . . . .

permeable . . . .

physical weathering . . . .

plucking . . . .

plunge pool . . . .

porous . . . .

pyramidal peak . . . .

quarry . . . .

reservoir . . . .

river basin . . . .

river cliff . . . .

run-off . . . .

saltation . . . .

scree . . . .

sedimentary rock . . . .

slip-off slope (river beach) . . . .

solution . . . .

source . . . .

spit . . . .

stack . . . .

stump . . . .

suspension . . . .

thalweg . . . .

traction . . . .

transportation . . . .

tributary . . . .

truncated spur . . . .

v-shaped valley . . . .

waterfall . . . .

watershed . . . .

watertable . . . .

weathering . . . .

Remember: items in *italics* will **not** be examined from Spring 2011. All items will be examined until Summer 2010.

Chapter 3: Environmental issues

- **Sustainable development** – using resources or areas of land in such a way that they will not run out or be damaged for future generations. For example, sustainable fishing would involve only catching breeds which are plentiful. Developing a school in a sustainable way would mean encouraging children to walk to school if possible, turning lights and computers off when not in use and making sure recycling was taking place. Sustainable tourism would be allowing tourists to visit a place to boost the economy, without causing any damage to the environment.

- **Stewardship** – looking after resources in a sustainable way so that they exist for future generations.

3.1 The purpose of national parks in the UK

National parks were established in 1949 by the government to:

- Protect beautiful areas of countryside from development.

- Preserve ways of life for people.

- Encourage the public to enjoy outdoor pursuits and visit areas of their countryside.

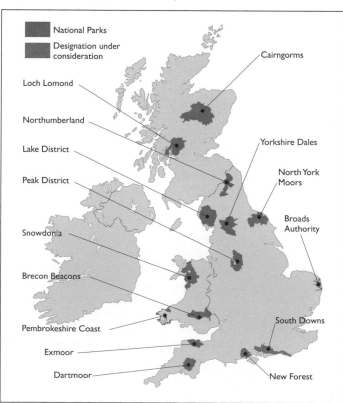

Fig. 3.1.1: National park locations in the UK

They are maintained by the National Parks Authority (NPA). The land is owned by farmers, the National Trust and the Ministry of Defence.

N.B. Proposed new national park: South Downs.

Case study 3.1 – Sustainable development in the Yorkshire Dales National Park

The Yorkshire Dales gained national park status in 1954. It is located in the Pennines in the north of England in the counties of North Yorkshire and Cumbria.

You should be able to place your study area of sustainable development on a map (see map of UK on page 116).

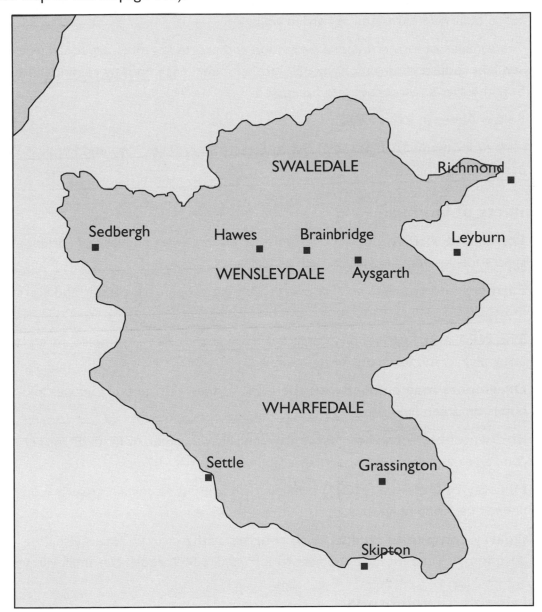

Fig. 3.1.2: Yorkshire Dales National Park

Main attractions

- Limestone (karst scenery) capped with milstone grit, which forms the Three Peaks (700 m).
- Limestone scenery such as Malham Cove, White Scar Caves and Gaping Gill, which are popular sites for potholing.

61

- In the west are the Howgills, grassy rounded hills with deep ravines.

- Drumlin fields at Ribblehead.

- Post-glacial lakes at Malham Tarn and Semerwater.

- Waterfalls such as Aysgarth Falls, Cautley Spout, High Force and Janet's Foss.

- Beautiful villages such as Malham.

- Rare flower-rich hay meadows and limestone woodland and scrub.

- Stone built field barns and dry stone walls.

- The remains of former mineral extraction and processing sites, especially lead and lime industry remains. Many mills are left behind as imposing reminders of how the area's resources were harnessed.

- Bolton Abbey in Wharfedale.

- Named footpaths such as the Coast to Coast route, Dales Way and Pennine Way pass through the Dales.

Conflicts of land use

- **Locals and tourists** conflict over noise levels in villages and lack of parking spaces for residents in villages such as Malham.

- **Farmers and tourists** conflict over leaving gates open, trespassing and scaring livestock.

- **The NPA and tourists** may conflict over vegetation being trampled, rare plants being picked and footpaths being trampled.

- **Developers may conflict with the NPA** as they wish to build houses and hotels on green field sites.

- **Bird watchers (ornithologists)** may conflict with other tourists or quarry companies as the excess noise may scare off the birds.

- **Ministry of Defence (MOD)** conflicts with tourists as certain areas are out of bounds for firing ranges.

- **Quarry companies conflict with tourists** as the quarry creates visual pollution; also the locals may object to lorries driving through the small villages.

Sustainable development

The aim of the Yorkshire National Park Authority is to ensure that visitors to the national park use and enjoy it, but at the same time to conserve it for future generations. The management of the national park addresses the conflicts of land use in the following ways:

- **Footpath erosion and vegetation trampling** – the NPA has built steps at Malham Cove; bare parts are reseeded; signs are erected.

- **Traffic congestion** – the NPA has created a park-and-ride system in Malham with free, guided walks for those who arrive by bus; parking restrictions have been introduced in the village.

- **Disturbance of habitats, picking rare flowers** – the NPA educates the public at Malham Park Information Centre.

Case study 3.2 – Sustainable development in Exmoor National Park

Exmoor gained national park status in 1954. It is located in the south-west of England in the counties of Devon (29%), and Somerset (71%).

You should be able to place your study area of sustainable development on a map (see map of UK on page 116).

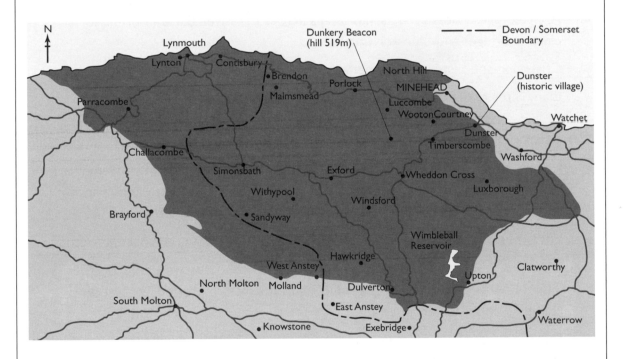

Fig. 3.1.3: Exmoor National Park

Main attractions

- Spectacular moorland, hills and valleys (area made of red sandstone).

- Many secluded bays and spectacular cliffs; Exmoor has the highest coastline in Britain (314 m above sea level at Culbone Hill).

- Stunning hills and valleys (Dunkery Beacon 519 m above sea level and the Valley of the Rocks – just west of Lynton).

- 1005 km of footpaths to hike and many mountain-bike trails.

- 55 km of coast line (the South West Coastal path starts in Exmoor).

- High coastal waterfalls, e.g. Hollow Brook at Martinhoe.

- Beaches at Combe Martin and Lynemouth.

- Plant species in Exmoor which are found nowhere else (two species of Whitebeam trees).

- Snowdrop Valley, near Wheddon Cross (a valley full of snowdrops).

- Rare species of animal (red deer and Exmoor pony – worldwide these ponies are rarer than the giant panda!).

- National stronghold of the Heath Fritillary butterfly.

- Most extensive broad-leaf wooded valleys in Britain.

- 243 species of birds.

- Wimball Lake water-sports location.

- Archaeological sites such as Tarr Steps across the River Barle (a prehistoric clapper bridge) and Dunster Castle.

- Charming and historic settlements such as Dunster.

- Many Sites of Special Scientific Interest (SSSIs).

Conflicts of land use

- **Locals and tourists** may conflict as house prices and prices of convenience goods in shops increase. Narrow roads become congested, residents' parking spaces are taken, shops and services become more suited to tourists.

- **Farmers and tourists** may conflict as gates are left open, trespassing occurs and livestock are scared.

- **The NPA and tourists** may conflict as footpaths are eroded, vegetation is trampled and litter dropped.

- **Developers** may conflict with the locals and the NPA as the developer will want to make money from building hotels and second homes.

- **Bird watchers (ornothologists)** may conflict with mountain bikers as noise may disturb birds.

N.B. If your national park is used for quarrying or by the MOD, there will be more conflicts.

Sustainable development

The aim of the Exmoor National Park Authority is to ensure that visitors to the national park use and enjoy it, but at the same time to conserve it for future generations. The management of the national park addresses the conflicts of land use in the following ways:

- Building of a **visitor information centre** at Dunster has helped educate the tourists to conserve the environment. The locals may have preferred a small supermarket to be built but probably are keen that tourists are attracted to boost the economy.

- **Green tourism leaflet** which encourages tourists to purchase locally produced goods, explains that they should follow the country code, engage in quiet activities and walk and use public transport rather than drive. This has the effect of boosting the sales of local farm goods and conserves the environment keeping the NPA and locals happy.

- **Exmoor Paths Partnership** is a group of volunteers who rebuild the paths of Exmoor. This has a positive effect on the area, as areas away from the paths are less trampled and less trespassing will occur. The locals also benefit from well-maintained paths.

- Developing other **honeypot sites** spreads out the economic benefits of tourism but could bring the problems associated with tourism to other parts of Exmoor.

- **Park and Ride** system at Snowdrop Valley has a positive effect as there is less traffic congestion on the narrow lanes and therefore less environmental pollution.

- Using conservation techniques, such as the **culverts** (stone or wood structures running across a path to divert water to the vegetation at the side of the path) on Dunkery Beacon, which prevent the formation of gullies. This avoids the path becoming a 'scar' which is difficult to walk on, and thus avoids the necessity of forming a new path.

- **Fertilising of grass and reseeding** where vegetation has been trampled. This benefits the ecosystem as vegetation can grow to bind the soil, increasing infiltration and reducing soil erosion and gully formation.

In Exmoor sustainable recreation (development) is occurring as the number of visitors is not as high as in other national parks. The type of visitor tends to be an 'eco-tourist' and the Exmoor National Park Authority are carrying out some successful management techniques.

Case study notes

Use this page to make notes on what you have learned about environmental issues.

Perhaps draw a box and bubble flow chart to help you revise. For help with these see *Study Skills* by Elizabeth Holtom, published by Galore Park.

Sample question

Try these sample questions for yourself. Suggested answers are given at the back of the book.

Q. 3.1 For a national park which you have studied, explain what conflicts are occurring. (4)

3.2 Explain how an area which you have studied is being sustainably developed. (6)

Summary

You should now know the following:

1. The purpose of national parks in the UK.

2. The sustainable development issues in your chosen area (national park).

Test yourself

Before moving on to the next chapter, make sure you can answer the following questions. The answers to questions 1–3 are at the back of the book.

1.   What is sustainable development?

2.   What is a national park?

3.   Explain why national parks have been created in the UK.

4.   Fill in this glossary list in pencil and ask your teacher to check you have filled it in correctly.

eco-tourism ....

energy ....

environment ....

habitat ....

honeypot site ....

landfill ....

national park ....

National Park Authority ....

pollution ....

SSSI ....

stewardship ....

sustainable development ....

Remember: items in *italics* will **not** be examined from Spring 2011.

Chapter 4: Economic geography

- **Primary industry** – extracting raw materials from the earth, e.g. farming, mining, fishing or forestry.

- **Secondary industry** – a manufacturing industry where raw materials are made into goods, e.g. baker, car-factory worker.

- **Tertiary industry** – a service industry selling goods or providing a service, e.g. doctor, lawyer, banker.

- **Quaternary industry** – a knowledge-based industry such as research and development into high-tech goods, e.g. research scientist.

4.1 Employment structure

The employment structure of a country is determined by the percentage of the workforce employed in each of the four types of industry: primary, secondary, tertiary and quaternary. An LEDC will have a different employment structure to that of an MEDC.

4.2 Location of an industry

During the last century in Britain, traditional heavy industries, e.g. iron and steel, were located next to coalfields (for power supply), raw materials and railways. But today's industries in Britain tend to be far less tied with regard to their location. They are generally high-tech industries. However, decisions are still made as to where to locate, and the following are considerations for the owners of the companies.

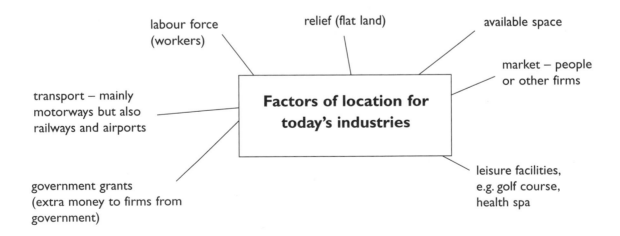

Fig. 4.2.1: Factors affecting location of industry

Sample question

Try these sample questions for yourself. The answers are given at the back of the book.

Q. 4.1. Why are fewer people involved in primary industry in Britain today than in the last century? (2)

4.2. What evidence of tertiary industry could you find on an OS map? (3)

4.3 Globalisation

The old style economic location model has become defunct as **low labour costs** have come to be the most important factor of location. Proximity to raw materials, energy supply and market are no longer as important as markets are now seen to be global; goods can now be transported easily and there is a ubiquitous energy supply available.

Globalisation is the way in which companies, ideas and lifestyles are spreading more and more around the world. This is helped by improvements in transport and communication. Globalisation affects us, what we eat, what we wear and what we watch on TV – when we decide these things it affects people thousands of miles away in different countries. Examples: Our cuisine is influenced by other countries, such as India. We watch TV shows made in the USA like 'Friends'.

Transnational corporation (TNC) or **multinational corporation (MNC)** – a company which has branches in many countries.

Case study 4.1 – Global economic activity: The global fashion industry (focus NIKE)

Make sure that you can mark these places onto a blank world map. These are all of the places involved in the transnational corporation Nike.

- Headquarters – Oregon (USA).

- Nike shops – these are mainly located in southern and western Europe, also Asia and North America (very few in South America or Africa).

- Sales – these are highest in Canada, USA and Europe.

- Manufacturing – this takes place in 40 countries. Clothing is mainly made in the Asia Pacific area and footwear in China, Indonesia, Vietnam and Thailand (1% of footwear is made in Italy).

- No Nike clothing or footwear is made in the USA.

Why is Nike a TNC and why has production spread in this way?

- Large market – advertising is everywhere and people feel they *must* get the brand, therefore the number of countries with shops and the number of shops have expanded.

- Lower costs – manufacture occurs in LEDCs as wages here are lower, land is cheaper to buy, the workforce are more flexible and access can be gained to global markets as well as the avoidance of trade restrictions.

- Nike has sub-contracted factories in LEDCs to make their goods rather than build their own factories.

Why has Nike become important on a Global scale?

- Nike employs 25 000 people directly and one million others are involved in making, supplying and selling goods.

- In the year 2000, 70% of 16-24 year olds in the UK bought at least one Nike product.

- In 2004, Nike made $1.6 billion profit!

- In 2004, Nike paid athletes and sports teams $1.7 billion to wear their gear.

- Nike employs sports scientists.

- Nike has a web site, giving worldwide access.

How has globalisation helped Nike develop?

- Transport improvements have allowed goods to be made in LEDCs (thereby saving costs) which can then be transported quickly to MEDCs. This increases Nike's profit.

- Transport improvements have also allowed managers to travel around the world quickly to visit factories and shops or to attend meetings.

- Email, fax and mobile phones enable easy communication between HQ and the shops and factories.

- Internet advertising and television have broadened marketing and increased sales.

- Global sports stars that are sponsored by Nike can be seen all over the world and therefore people from many countries wish to buy the items they are wearing.

 Extra material is required here for pupils taking exams from Spring 2011 onwards. This is available to download from www.galorepark.co.uk

How does all this affect the LEDCs?

Benefits	Problems
Provides jobs	Can cause environmental damage and pollution
Attracts others to set up TNCs	Influences host government's decisions
Increases country's wealth	Pays low wages (£4 for 12-hour day)
Provides expert managers	Encourages poor working conditions
May provide healthcare benefits for workers	Slows down LEDCs developing their own industries
Uses latest technology	Often workers are sacked without any notice
Increases exports	Some sweat shops develop
Increases skills of country's workforce	
Helps improve country's roads and power supply	

How does all this affect the MEDCs?

Benefits	Problems
Greater profit made through cheap labour costs	Loss of manufacturing jobs in the MEDC
Consumers get cheaper products and greater choice	
Spreads the MEDC's influence	

Case study notes

Use this page to make notes on what you have learned about your economic geography case studies.

Perhaps draw a box and bubble flow chart to help you revise. For help with these see *Study Skills* by Elizabeth Holtom, published by Galore Park.

Summary

You should now know the following:

1. How the employment structure of a country is determined.

2. The decisions behind where industries decide to locate.

3. The effect of globalisation on industry.

Test yourself

Before moving on to the next chapter, make sure you can answer the following questions. The answers to questions 1–3 are at the back of the book.

1. What is tertiary industry?

2. What is globalisation?

3. What is a transnational company?

4. Fill in this glossary list in pencil and ask your teacher to check you have filled it in correctly.

2011

agriculture . . . .

arable . . . .

business park . . . .

economic activity . . . .

eco-tourism . . . .

globalisation . . . .

2011

hectare . . . .

Industrial Revolution 2011

irrigation ....

LEDC ....

manufacturing industry 2011

market ....

MEDC 2011

mining ....

multi-national corporation (MNC) ....

newly industrialised country (NIC) 2011

pastoral ....

primary industry ....

quaternary industry ....

quota ....

raw material ....

retail ....

science park 2011

secondary industry ....

service industry 2011

tertiary industry ....

tourism ....

transnational corporation (TNC) ....

Remember: items in *italics* will **not** be examined from Spring 2011.

Chapter 5: Settlement geography

5.1 Functions of a settlement

- **Residential** – place for living.
- **Industrial** – location of factories, etc. (these days in out-of-town locations in the outer suburbs).
- **Commercial** – shopping centres, cinemas, leisure centres, etc.
- **Service functions** – schools, hospitals, libraries, etc.

5.2 Reasons for the site or situation of a settlement

- **Site** – the exact physical location of a settlement.
- **Situation** – the setting of a settlement in relation to surrounding features (its environs).

Remember that most settlements grew up in ancient times, before motorways and tourism! The following had to be considered:

- **Relief** – area needed to be high to be safe from flooding but low enough to be sheltered from winds.
- **Transport** – fording or bridging points of rivers, crossroads (originally tracks rather than roads) and coasts.
- **Soil** – the deeper and more fertile, the better for agriculture.
- **Water supply** – for cooking, cleaning and drinking.
- **Wood** – for building and fuel.
- **Defence** – hilltops, marshes and meander bends created protection from enemies.

5.3 London as a settlement

Why is London in this location?

The original locational factors were:

- dry point site – island in marsh land
- good water supply (Thames)
- fording and bridging point
- forests nearby to provide building materials.

What are London's present-day functions?

- port
- industrial
- commercial
- tourism
- financial
- administrative
- service
- residential

Fig. 5.3.1: London's location and functions

5.4 Settlement hierarchy

Settlements can be ranked in order – a hierarchy. The order within the hierarchy is decided by population, area, and range and number of services.

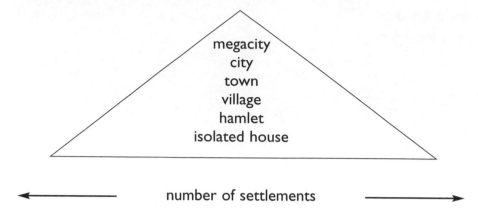

Fig. 5.4.1: The settlement hierarchy

N.B. A megacity has a population of over 10 million.

The larger the settlement, the more services it will have.

Settlement	Services
hamlet	perhaps none
village	church, public house, convenience shop (although many are disappearing), primary school
town	several shops, churches, secondary school, dentist, bank, small hospital (although fewer and fewer exist in towns)
city	cathedral, large railway station, large shopping centre, large hospital, specialist shops, museum

5.5 Shopping hierarchy

Within a city the shops/shopping areas can be classified into a hierarchy depending on their importance and how many other similar areas there are in the city.

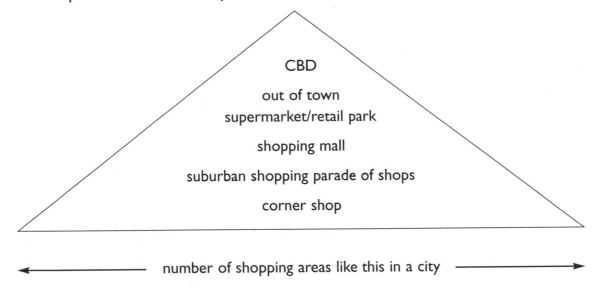

Important shopping words

Shopping word	Definition
sphere of influence	the area around a shop, settlement or service from which customers come
range	the maximum distance someone will travel to use a shop, service or settlement
threshold	the minimum number of customers required to keep a shop or service in business; for example, a theatre would have a higher threshold than a newsagents
convenience goods	goods which are bought regularly, are cheap and for which you would not be prepared to travel far to buy; for example a newspaper, chocolate bar or a loaf of bread
comparison goods	goods for which you would be prepared to travel further to buy, you would shop around for to get the best price and you do not need to buy regularly; for example a car, a computer or a suit

5.6 Settlement patterns

Settlements develop in a pattern. Many settlements contain a mixture of these shapes. The diagrams below show village settlement patterns.

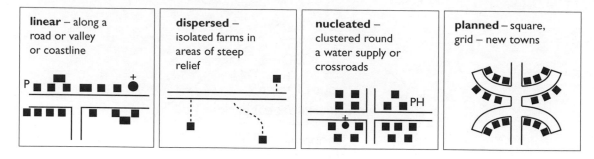

Fig. 5.6.1: The different settlement patterns

Many settlements have linear sections (ribbon developments), as houses are built along transport routes. As transport improved in Britain in the 1920s, people could live further from work, and urban sprawl occurred together with linear developments along new transport routes. Green belts (where planning permission is limited) were introduced to control urban sprawl.

2011

5.7 Rural decline and suburbanisation

Many villages have experienced a growth in population but a decline in services. They have lost their:

- Village shop.
- Bank.
- Post office.
- Primary school.
- Daily bus service.

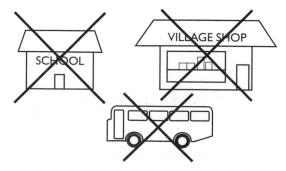

Fig. 5.7.1: Rural decline

Causes

- New housing estates built to house commuters – urban to rural migration for better standard of living.
- Villages suburbanised.

- Commuters not in village in daytime to use services (they use services in the town or city where they work).

- Out-of-town superstores, rather than the village shop, used by commuters with cars (one-stop shopping).

An example – Thurston Village

Location: East Anglia, 4 miles from Bury St Edmunds

1801	1846	1960	1991	2003
Population: 345	Population: 600	Population: 740	Population: 2610	Population: 5000
Inhabitants worked in agriculture	Railway built; more people came; village expanded	A45 was widened; commuting to Bury was easier; more commuters arrived	Few people worked in Thurston; most worked and shopped in Bury St Edmunds; village shop closed	Even fewer work in Thurston

Although the population has risen, the services provided in Thurston have declined.

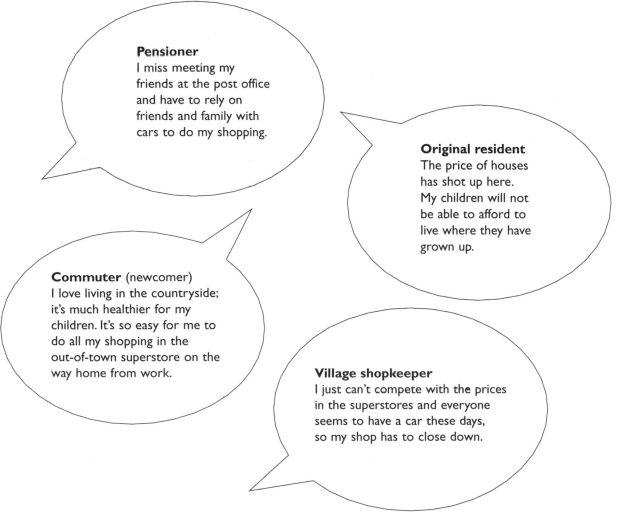

Fig. 5.7.2: The effects of rural decline and suburbanisation

81

Sample question

Try this sample question for yourself. A suggested answer is given at the back of the book.

Q. 5.1 Why would a city have a greater number of shops and services than a village? (5)

5.8 Urban land use zones

Concentric ring model – devised by Burgess in the 1920s and based on Chicago.

- **City centre** or **central business district (CBD):** commercial land use, shops and offices, but no houses; little open space; very accessible because transport routes meet up.

- **Inner city zone of transition** or **twilight zone:** old industrial land plus densely packed nineteenth-century terraced houses; some of the industry and terraced houses have been knocked down and replaced with high-rise flats; this is called urban redevelopment.

- **Inner suburbs:** semi-detached houses built 1930s–1950s (residential).

- **Outer suburbs:** large, detached, low-density housing built since the 1960s (residential); cul-de-sacs evident; also modern light industrial estates.

The price of land decreases the further away from the CBD you go. Many cities in Great Britain have green belts round them where planning regulations restrict building, helping to prevent urban sprawl.

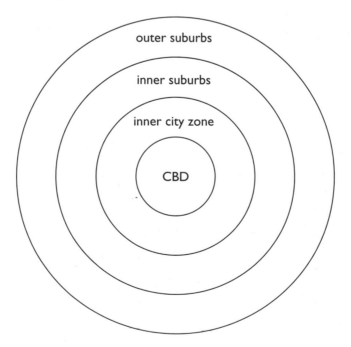

Fig. 5.8.1: The concentric ring model

5.9 Conflicts over land use

Many large shopping centres (e.g. Bluewater) and office developments are built on out-of-town locations, e.g. greenfield sites. Offices often cluster on business or science parks.

Reasons for choosing these locations

- Good access to motorways / ring roads for deliveries and customers.
- More room for car parks / expansion.
- Cheaper land.
- Pleasant environment.
- Wide choice of housing in suburbs.
- No opposition from CBD shop owners.

Groups which conflict

- **Local residents** – may be happy as they can use new shops; may be cross due to noise and congestion.
- **Shopkeepers from CBD** – are annoyed that new shopping centre takes customers away from them.
- **Developers** – are pleased as they make money from developing the site.
- **Environmentalists** – are angry as new shopping centre is often / could be on rural land outside the town which was providing a habitat for wildlife.

5.10 Changing function of an urban area

London's Docklands formed Britain's busiest port until the 1950s but changes have occurred since then.

Reasons for change

- Ships too large for docks.
- New forms of transport, e.g. trucks.
- Containerisation – little need for dockers.

Effects of change

- Docks became derelict.
- Unemployment rose.
- Terraced housing fell into disrepair.
- Transport links worsened.
- Service and leisure amenities declined.

Redevelopment

LDDC (London Docklands Development Corporation) was set up in July 1981 to:

- Attract new industries (financial and printing), e.g. the Guardian.
- Improve transport, e.g. Docklands Light Railway, City Airport and extension to the Jubilee Line.
- Build new office blocks.
- Create 20 000 new homes.
- Improve services and recreation, e.g. indoor sports centre and parkland.

Problems

- Jobs now available do not fit the skills of the ex-dockers.
- Newcomers do not mix with the original East-Enders; the close-knit community is broken up.
- Hospitals or care homes do not provide adequately for the elderly.

5.11 Growth in London (MEDC)

Reasons for growth

- More and better-paid jobs, e.g. jobs in the City.
- More and better services, e.g. schools, hospitals.
- Greater choice of housing.
- Arrival of many ethnic groups to join friends or family.
- Greater choice of entertainment, social and cultural amenities.

Problems of growth

- Due to pressure on green belt, increased urban sprawl in Greater London.
- Core and periphery effect even greater in UK.
- Overcrowding in schools and waiting lists for hospitals.
- Traffic congestion and other environmental and health problems.
- Increased crime and vandalism.
- Potential problems associated with ethnic minorities.

Solutions

- Congestion charge.
- Housing subsidies for key workers.
- Use of more brownfield rather than greenfield sites for development.
- Teaching of cultural differences in schools.

Summary

You should now know the following:

1. The different functions of a settlement.

2. The reasons why locations were chosen for particular settlements.

3. The settlement hierarchy and different settlement patterns.

4. *The causes and effects of rural decline.*

5. *The concentric ring model for urban land use zones.*

6. *The conflicts that may arise over land use.*

7. *How and why the function of an urban area may change.*

8. *The reasons behind London's growth, the problems that have occurred and how these have been addressed.*

Test yourself

Before moving on to the next chapter, make sure you can answer the following questions. The answers to questions 1–3 are at the back of the book.

1. What is a megacity?

2. What types of land use would you expect to find in the centre of a typical British city?

3. Fill in the blanks, choosing suitable words from those given below.

services   transportation   busiest   unemployment   luxury

skills   industry   parkland

In the 1950s the Docklands was one of the .... ports in the world. Ships on the River Thames transported wood, coal and food. New forms of .... which were more efficient were invented, ships became too large to sail up the Thames and goods were transported in huge containers; the area declined and there was high .... The London Docklands Development Corporation was set up to try to alleviate the problems. It attracted new .... and improved the transport links as well as creating new flats. It also improved many of the services and created .... However the LDDC has suffered much criticism in that the new jobs created required .... which the ex-dockers did not have. The new .... flats were too expensive for the

locals. The feeling between the newcomers and the original residents was uneasy.

The ex-dockers felt that more care could have been put into creating jobs,

housing and .... which are more suitable to their needs.

4. Fill in this glossary list in pencil and ask your teacher to check you have filled it
in correctly.

brownfield site ....

business park ....

central business district (CBD) ....

commercial land use ....

comparison goods ....

convenience goods ....

cul-de-sac ....

detached housing ....

dispersed ....

favela ....

green belt ....

greenfield site ....

function ....

hamlet ....

hierarchy ....

inner city ....

inner suburbs ....

land use ....

LEDC ....

linear . . . .

MEDC . . . .

megacity . . . .

nucleated . . . .

outer suburbs . . . .

range . . . .

recreational land use . . . .

residential land use . . . .

retail . . . .

rural . . . .

semi-detached housing . . . .

settlement . . . .

settlement pattern . . . .

shanty town . . . .

site . . . .

situation . . . .

sphere of influence . . . .

suburbanisation . . . .

terraced housing . . . .

threshold . . . .

urban . . . .

urban renewal / redevelopment . . . .

urbanisation . . . .

Chapter 6: Earthquakes and volcanoes

- **Tectonic plates** – huge slabs of rock which form the Earth's crust and which float on the mantle; the lightest and thickest plates are called **continental crust** and form land; the thinner but heavier crust is called **oceanic crust** and has sea over it.

- **Mid-Atlantic Ridge** – a constructive plate boundary which runs down the middle of the Atlantic Ocean; there is a chain of volcanic islands on this boundary.

- **Pacific Ring of Fire** – the name given to the destructive plate boundary which forms a band of earthquakes and volcanoes round the edge of the Pacific Ocean.

6.1 Types of plate boundary

Constructive plate boundary

- Two plates move apart.

- Magma rises to surface, due to gas bubbles in it which are lighter than the surrounding rock.

- Volcanoes are formed.

- Gentle eruptions occur which may continue for years.

N.B. Most constructive boundaries are under the sea and form chains of volcanic islands (the Mid-Atlantic Ridge is the most famous).

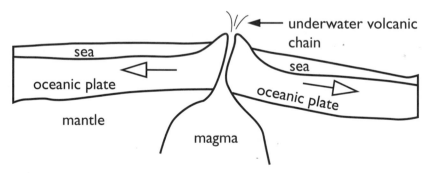

Fig. 6.1.1: Constructive plate boundary

Destructive plate boundary

- Oceanic and continental plates collide.

- Heavier oceanic plate sinks under the continental one into what is known as a subduction zone.

- Melted crust rises (due to the gas bubbles in the magma which makes it lighter than the surrounding rock) to form explosive, dangerous volcanoes.

- When plates rub, friction occurs, leading to earthquakes.

N.B. The most famous destructive boundary is the Pacific Ring of Fire. A destructive plate boundary was also the cause of the Sonfrière Hills Volcano, Montserrat.

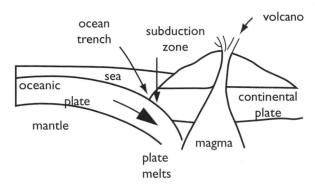

Fig. 6.1.2: Destructive plate boundary

Conservative plate boundary

- Tectonic plates slide past each other.
- Plates become locked and tension builds up over years.
- Rocks break and jerk forward causing powerful earthquakes.

N.B. The most famous of these is the San Andreas fault.

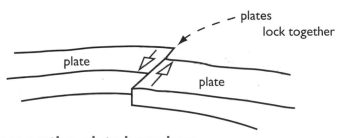

Fig. 6.1.3: Conservative plate boundary

Collision boundary

- Two continental plates push together.
- Neither sinks as they are made from light rock.
- Plates buckle to form fold mountains (Himalayas being the most famous).
- No volcanoes but violent earthquakes.

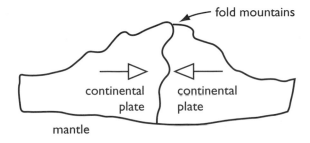

Fig. 6.1.4: Collision plate boundary

6.2 Types of volcano

Composite volcanoes

- Occur in areas of destructive plate boundaries.

- Eruption is violent, ejecting thick and sticky lava.

- Ash and lava are ejected into the air and descend as slow-flowing, thick lava, then the process is repeated – building up layers of ash and lava.

- Pyroclastic flows (hot gas and ash) travelling more than 100 mph can flatten and burn everything in their path.

- Lahars (melted ice or rain mixed with ash) can occur.

- Thick layers of ash leave areas uninhabitable.

- Tsunamis can cause devastation miles away from the site of the eruption.

Examples of composite volcanoes are the Soufrière Hills Volcano, Montserrat and Mount Etna.

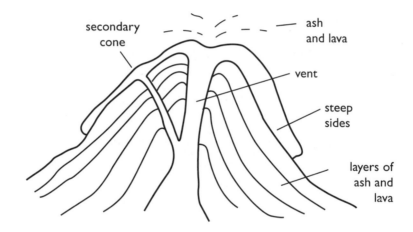

Fig. 6.2.1: Composite volcano

Shield volcanoes

- Occur in areas of constructive plate boundaries.

- Wide, gently-sloping volcanoes eject thin, runny lava.

- Eruptions are not explosive and are less likely to result in loss of life.

Examples of shield volcanoes are Iceland and Hawaii.

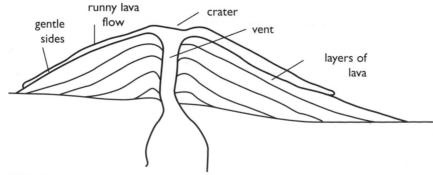

Fig. 6.2.2: Shield volcano

6.3 Reasons for the movement of plates

The movement of plates is called **continental drift**. Continental drift occurs due to the movement of the magma in the mantle below the plates. The movement of the magma is caused by convection currents generated by the immense heat at the Earth's core.

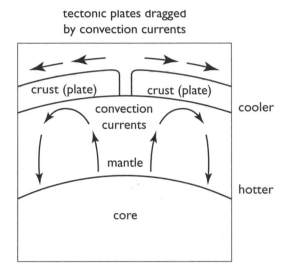

Fig. 6.3.1: Continental drift and plate movement

6.4 Immediate effects of a volcanic eruption

- **Ash fall.**

- **Mud flow (lahar)** – ash mixed with rain or melted glacial water.

- **Pyroclastic flow** – hot gas and ash rolling down cone.

- **Lava flow** – molten rock.

- **Pyroclastic bombs (volcanic bombs)** – lava cooling when ejected into air, falling as solid rock.

6.5 Methods of preparing for a volcanic eruption

- Hazard maps can be drawn (as in Montserrat) to show which areas are safest and which are most at risk.

- Lava flows can be diverted by channels or explosives, dammed or sprayed with cool water.

- People can be evacuated.

- Seismometers can record the earthquakes which occur as the magma rises.

- Tiltmeters can record changes in the shape of the volcano.

- Satellites can record the temperature and shape of volcanoes.

6.6 Why people live near volcanoes

- Tourism is generated by interest in volcanoes – boosts economy.

- Geothermal energy can be produced from the rising steam, e.g. Iceland, New Zealand.

- Fertile soil is produced by the weathering of volcanic ash (good for grapevines).

- Minerals, such as gold and diamonds, can be found.

6.7 Factors determining the severity of damage

- The type of plate boundary which has caused it – destructive plate boundaries cause violent volcanoes.

- Its proximity to a large settlement – those situated near large cities where population is dense cause greater numbers of deaths.

- The wealth of the country in which it erupts – an MEDC can afford scientific prediction instruments, a quick reaction force and good medical care for the injured.

Case study 6.1 – Soufrière Hills Volcano, Montserrat

Cause

- The Soufrière Hills Volcano is located on a destructive plate boundary of three plates: South America, North America and Caribbean. After a long period of dormancy it became active in 1995 and eruptions have continued to the present day.

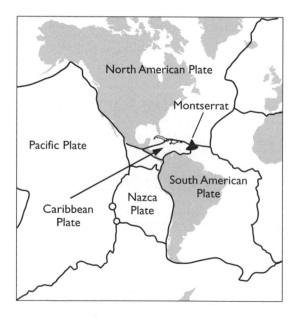

Fig. 6.7.1: Location of Soufrière Hills Volcano

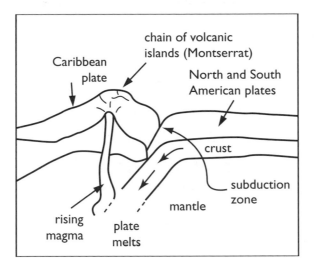

Fig. 6.7.2: Destructive plate boundary (North and South American and Caribbean plates)

Effects

Environmental

- Pyroclastic flow burned vegetation.

- Ash covered two thirds of the island.

- Wildlife disappeared.

- Coral reef and sea creatures died from the ash washed into the sea.

- New land was formed when the pyroclastic flow solidified in the sea.

Economic

- Agricultural economy ruined.

- Tourist economy ruined – airport closed.

Social

- Montserrat is a UK dependency therefore the UK is obliged to offer aid and assistance.

- 60% of housing destroyed.

- 23 people died in the pyroclastic flow of 25th June 1997.

- 8000 inhabitants left Montserrat for the UK and Antigua.

- Hospitals destroyed.

- Few schools left intact.

- Lack of clean water and sewerage facilities.

Human response

- Montserrat volcano observatory built to monitor volcano with seismometers and tiltmeters.

- Hazard map drawn up to highlight danger and safe zones.

- International aid received from the UK and other countries.

- Inhabitants evacuated to the UK and Antigua.

- There was a concert in the Royal Albert Hall to raise money. This money allowed the UK to send out HMS Liverpool with emergency showers and kitchen facilities for the islanders.

Case study 6.2 – The Kashmir Earthquake, 8th October 2005

Facts

- 7.6 magnitude earthquake which took place on Saturday 8th October at 09.25, local time.

- Epicentre was at Muzzaffarabad, the capital of the Kashmir region administered by Pakistan, 80km north-east of Islamabad.

- Strongest earthquake to hit the region in a century.

- Followed by 1,000,000 powerful aftershocks.

Cause

- The result of India's long-term, gradual, geological movement north into Asia at a speed of five centimetres a year, or one millimetre per week.

- The Indian plate is colliding with the Eurasian plate, creating a **collision boundary** (see Fig. 6.7.3).

- As both plates are continental neither is heavier than the other, therefore the plates converge and form fold mountains.

- As the plates push together they lock and, when the plates move, friction occurs. This friction makes the earth shake and this is the earthquake.

- The area where the earthquake starts underground is known as the focus. Directly above the focus, on the Earth's surface, is the epicentre.

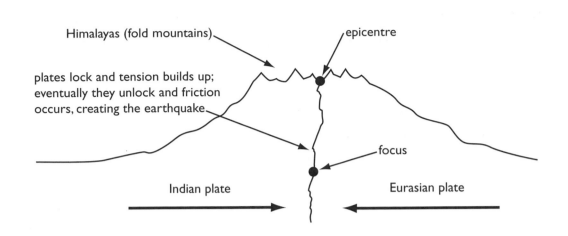

Fig. 6.7.3: Collision boundary

Effects

> Affected population: 3.5m
>
> Pakistan: 73,338 dead
>
> India: 1,360 dead
>
> Health facilities destroyed: 80%
>
> Area affected: 30,000 sq km

- The worst-hit areas were Pakistan-administered Kashmir and the eastern districts of the North-West Frontier Province.

- President Musharraf said: 'Many villages have been wiped off the face of the earth.'

- Children suffered the biggest number of casualties, as many had just started lessons when the earthquake struck and were killed when their schools collapsed. Entire generations of young people were wiped out in the areas worst hit.

- A 13 year old survivor said: 'We slept in the open fields last night. There were no tents, no food; everything is gone. We all rushed out only to see our house going down in front of our own eyes.'

- About 200 soldiers were thought to have been killed by landslides and falling debris.

- 6,000 schools and colleges were destroyed by the earthquake.

- All official buildings in the area collapsed.

- Landslides blocked all access roads to Muzaffarabad.

- No electricity or telephone lines were working.

- The once thriving town of **Balakot** suffered extensive damage.

Human response

- Tents, medicines, money and helicopters were provided by foreign NGOs, for example Oxfam, UNICEF and International Red Cross.

- Save the Children distributed 522 school kits containing teaching materials, notebooks, pencils, games and toys to schools and provided 80,000 textbooks.

- By Sunday some foreign rescue teams had arrived, equipped with specialised equipment such as CO_2 'sniffers', snake-eye cameras to move through the buildings, special listening equipment and specially trained dogs.

- Members of the International Rescue Corps used life-detecting sensors to locate a thirteen-year-old boy under the rubble.

- By 11th November the government had distributed 350,000 tents, 3.2m blankets, 3,000 tonnes of medicine and set up dozens of tent villages for those affected.

- With thousands dead, many in Kashmir were highly critical of the government's relief efforts, saying it was too little too late.

- The authorities encouraged people to make their new homes more resistant to earthquakes.

- Twelve housing reconstruction centres were set up around the region to help train people, resulting in over 75,000 people being given basic training to create homes which incorporate earthquake-resistant features.

- The UN agencies allocated $95.6m for 26 livelihood programmes, involving seed distribution, fertilisers, livestock, skill development and agriculture implants.

- More than 1.25m children in the region, who were not vaccinated before, were given shots against polio, meningitis and measles, as well as Vitamin A injections.

- Aid efforts enabled the setting up of a spinal cord injury rehabilitation facility in Islamabad for women and children, treating over 100 quadriplegic and paraplegic patients.

 Extra material is required here for pupils taking exams from Spring 2011 onwards. This is available to download from www.galorepark.co.uk

Case study notes

Use this page to make notes on what you have learned about your volcano or earthquake case study.

Perhaps draw a box and bubble flow chart to help you revise. For help with these see *Study Skills* by Elizabeth Holtom, published by Galore Park.

Sample questions

Try these sample questions for yourself, using the Soufrière Hills Volcano as your case study. Answers are given at the back of the book.

Q. 6.1 Locate the case study on the world map. (1)

6.2 Why did this volcano or earthquake occur? (4)

6.3 Locate two other volcanic areas on the world map. (2)

6.4 For an earthquake or a volcano which you have studied, describe the major effects which it has had on the surrounding area. (4)

6.5 Study the map below which shows the distribution of earthquakes and volcanoes around the world. (2)

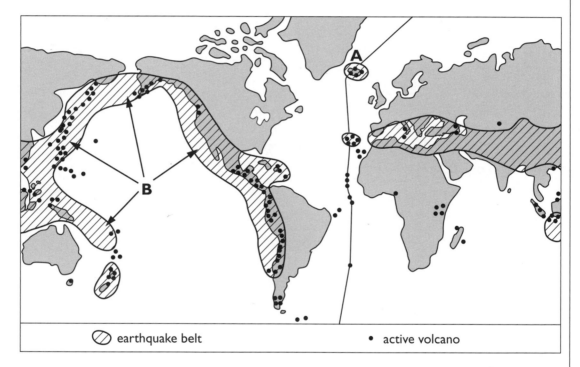

⬭ earthquake belt   • active volcano

Name areas **A** and **B** on the map.

A ....

B ....

6.6 Explain why, compared with an MEDC, an LEDC could suffer more severely from a volcanic eruption or an earthquake. (3)

Summary

You should now know the following:

1. The different types of plate boundaries.

2. *The different types of volcanoes.*

3. Why plates move.

4. The immediate effects of a volcanic eruption.

5. What can be done to prepare for a volcanic eruption.

6. The reasons why people live near volcanoes.

7. What determines the severity of the volcanic damage.

8. The cause and effects of one volcanic eruption or one earthquake.

Test yourself

Before moving on to the next chapter, make sure you can answer the following questions. The answers to questions 1–3 are at the back of the book.

1. Name the most famous destructive plate boundary.

2. *What type of volcanoes occur in Iceland and Hawaii?*

3. What instrument records the change in shape of a volcano?

4. Fill in this glossary with a pencil and ask your teacher to check you have filled it in correctly.

active . . . .

collision boundary . . . .

composite volcano . . . .

cone . . . .

conservative plate boundary . . . .

constructive plate boundary . . . .

continental drift . . . .

continental plate / crust . . . .

convection currents . . . .

core ....

crater ....

crust ....

destructive plate boundary ....

dormant ....

epicentre ....

eruption ....

extinct ....

focus ....

fold mountains ....

foreshock ....

geothermal energy ....

inner core ....

lahars ....

lava ....

magma ....

magma chamber ....

mantle ....

Mid-Atlantic Ridge ....

oceanic plate / crust ....

outer core ....

Pacific Ring of Fire ....

Pangea ....

pyroclastic flow . . . .

secondary cone . . . .

seismic wave . . . .

seismometer . . . .

shield volcano . . . .

subduction zone . . . .

tectonic plates . . . .

tiltmeter . . . .

tsunami . . . .

vent . . . .

volcanic bombs . . . .

Remember: items in *italics* will **not** be examined from Spring 2011. All items will be examined until Summer 2010.

Location maps

Remember: the locations in *italics* will **not** be examined from Spring 2011.

Map 1: UK, Great Britain and British Isles

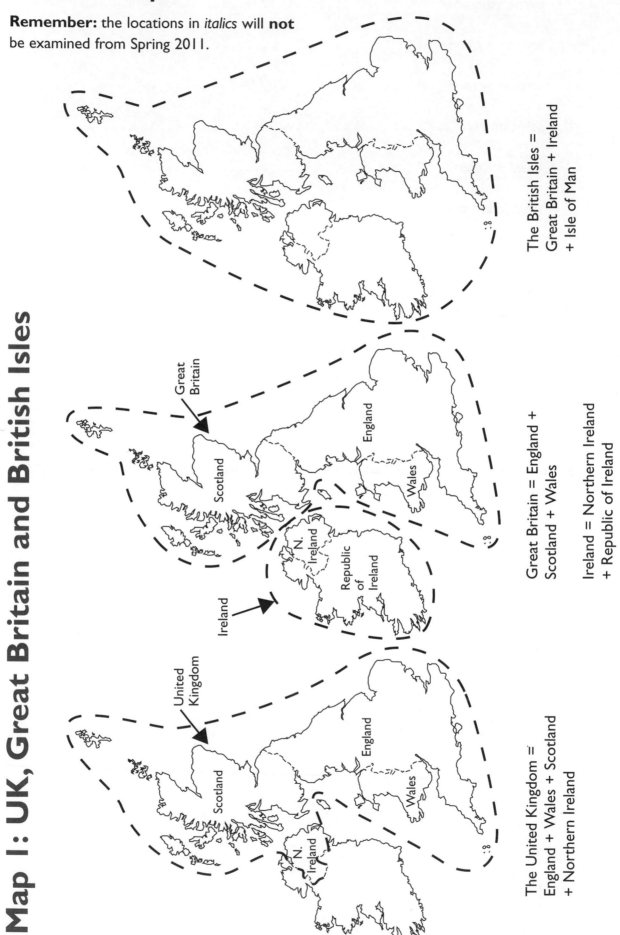

The British Isles = Great Britain + Ireland + Isle of Man

Great Britain = England + Scotland + Wales

Ireland = Northern Ireland + Republic of Ireland

The United Kingdom = England + Wales + Scotland + Northern Ireland

Map 2: National parks in Great Britain

Cairngorms

Loch Lomond
and the
Trossachs

Northumberland

Lake
District

North York Moors

Yorkshire
Dales

Peak
District

The
Broads

Snowdonia

Brecon
Beacons

Pembrokeshire
Coast

Exmoor

The South
Downs

New
Forest

Dartmoor

0   km   100

Map 3: British Isles

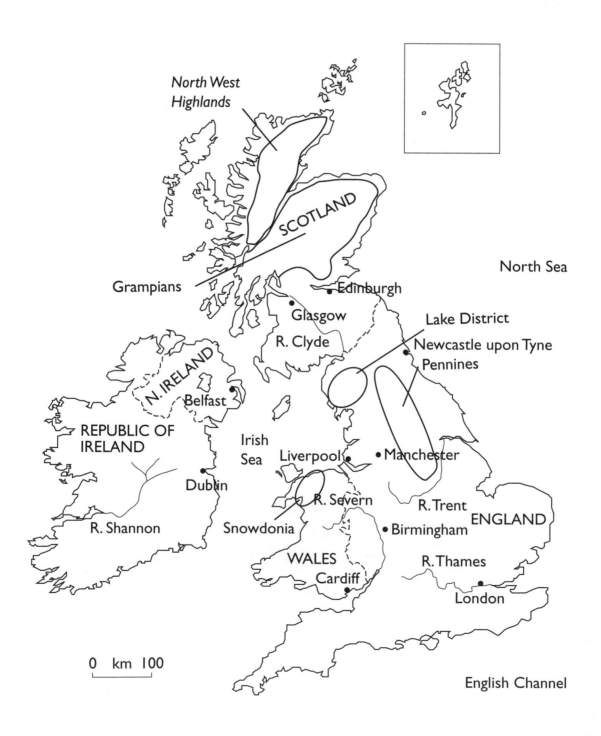

North West
Highlands

SCOTLAND

Grampians

North Sea

• Edinburgh

• Glasgow

R. Clyde

Lake District

Newcastle upon Tyne

Pennines

N. IRELAND

• Belfast

REPUBLIC OF
IRELAND

Irish
Sea

Liverpool •

• Manchester

Dublin •

R. Severn

R. Shannon

Snowdonia

R. Trent

ENGLAND

• Birmingham

WALES

Cardiff •

R. Thames

London •

0   km 100

English Channel

Map 4: Continents

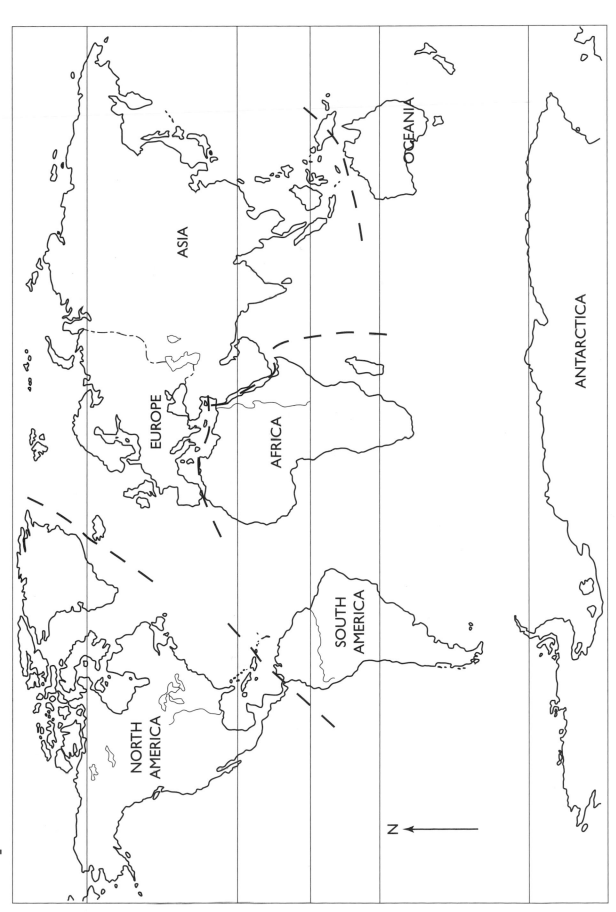

NORTH
AMERICA

EUROPE

ASIA

AFRICA

OCEANIA

SOUTH
AMERICA

ANTARCTICA

N

Map 5: Europe: physical geography

Arctic Ocean

North Atlantic Ocean

English Channel

R. Rhine

Alps

Pyrenees

Mt Etna

0   km   500

Map 6: The European Union: human geography

Map 7: Asia

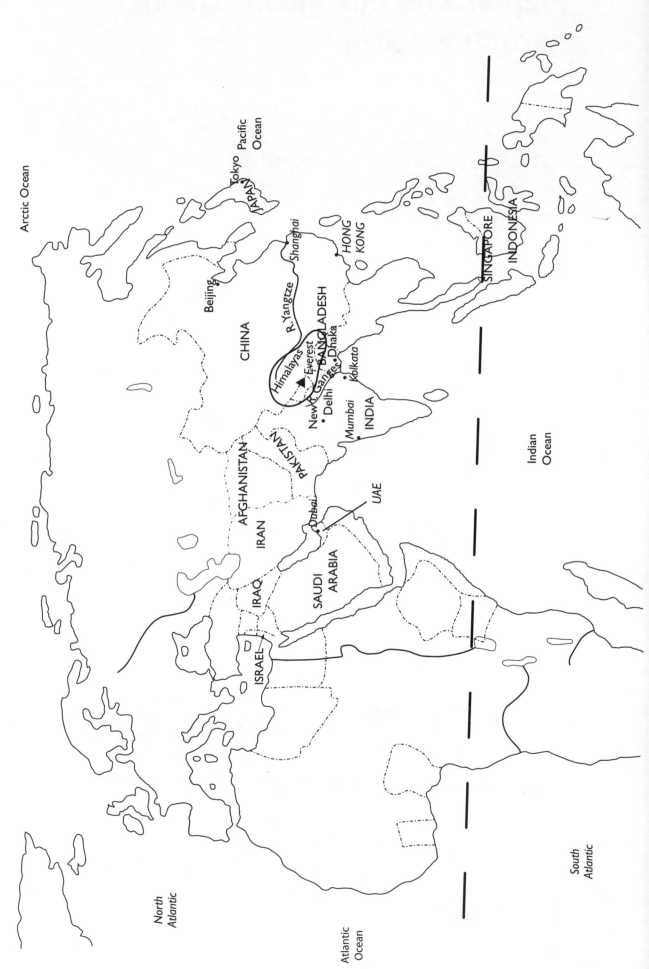

Map 8: Oceania

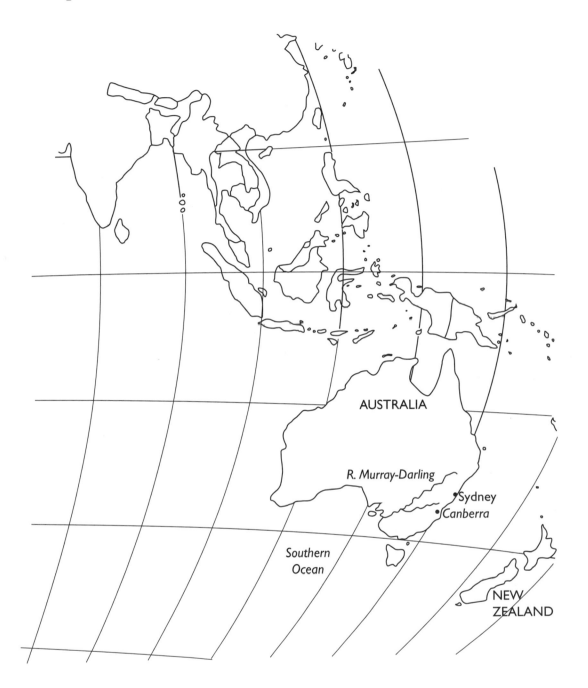

AUSTRALIA

R. Murray-Darling

•Sydney
•Canberra

Southern
Ocean

NEW
ZEALAND

Map 9: North and Central America

Rocky Mountains

CANADA

U.S.A.

San Francisco

Pacific
Ocean

Los Angeles

New York
Washington D.C.

Mississippi

MEXICO

Hawaii
Mauna Loa

Mexico
City

MONTSERRAT

0   km   1000

Caribbean
Sea

Map 10: South America

R.Amazon

PERU

Lima

BRAZIL

Andes

CHILE

Rio de Janeiro

São Paulo

ARGENTINA

South
Atlantic
Ocean

0   km   1000

Cape Horn

Map 11: Africa

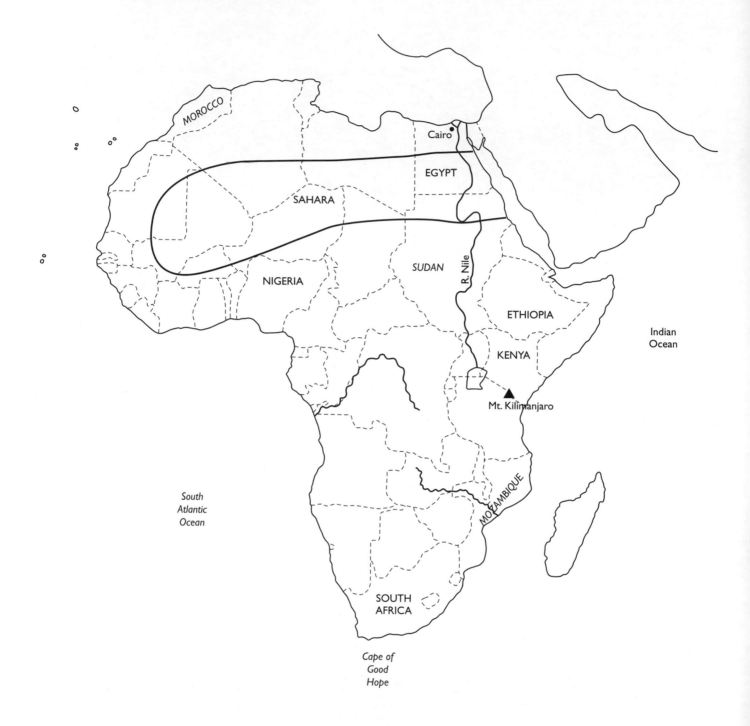

MOROCCO

Cairo

EGYPT

SAHARA

NIGERIA

SUDAN

R. Nile

ETHIOPIA

KENYA

▲
Mt. Kilimanjaro

Indian
Ocean

South
Atlantic
Ocean

MOZAMBIQUE

SOUTH
AFRICA

Cape of
Good
Hope

Map 12: Tropical rainforests and volcanoes

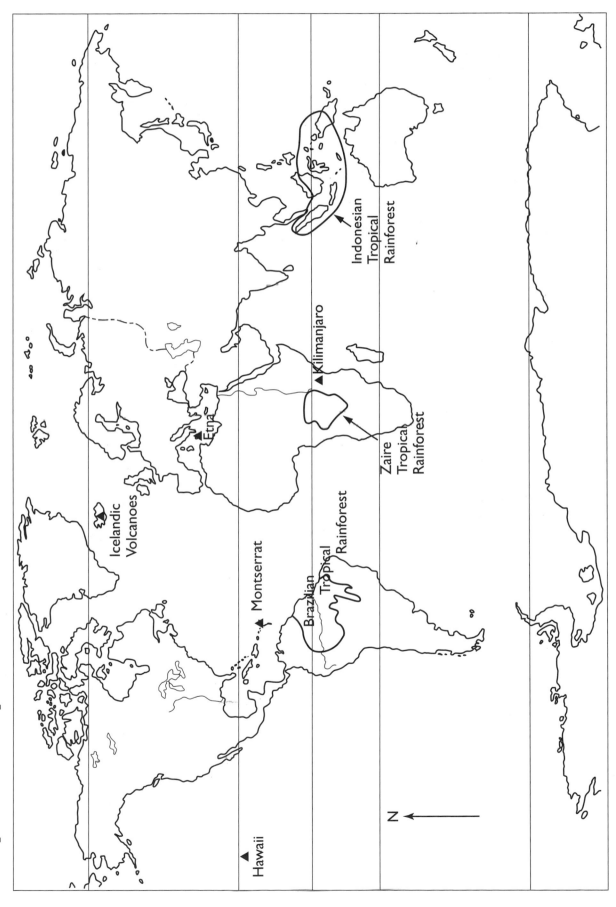

Map 13: General world features

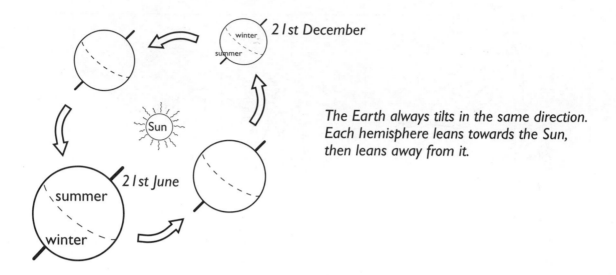

The Earth always tilts in the same direction. Each hemisphere leans towards the Sun, then leans away from it.

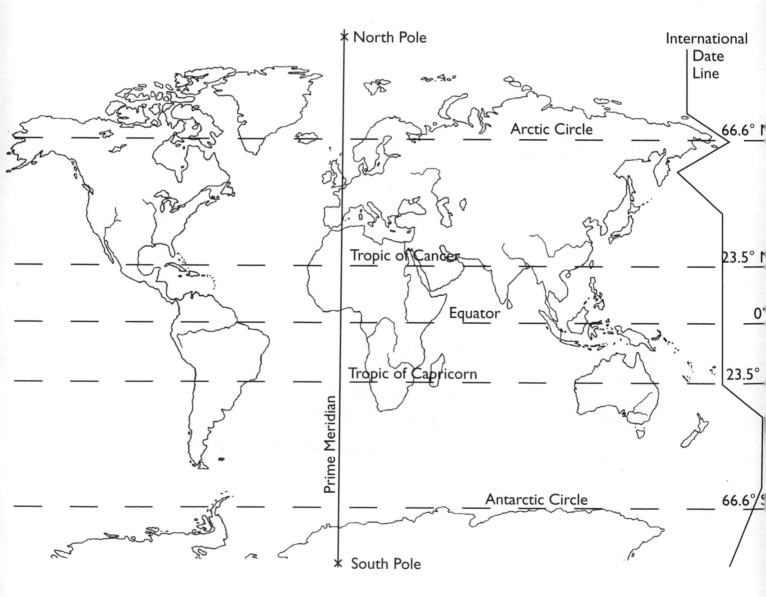

Blank maps

For pupils taking exams up to Summer 2010:

The following blank maps are for use with your case studies.

You must know the location of:

- *your volcano or earthquake;*
- *your flood;*
- *your weather hazard;*
- *your area which is being sustainably developed;*
- *your global industry.*

For pupils taking exams from Spring 2011:

The following blank maps are for use with any examples or mini case studies which you have used.

You must know the location of:

- your volcanic eruptions and earthquakes (one must be from a MEDC and one from a LEDC);
- your example of a managed location (e.g. a nature reserve or national park);
- your local economic activity and your economic activity in a LEDC.

 Additional blank maps are also available for download from the Galore Park website.

Blank map 1: British Isles – *case studies*

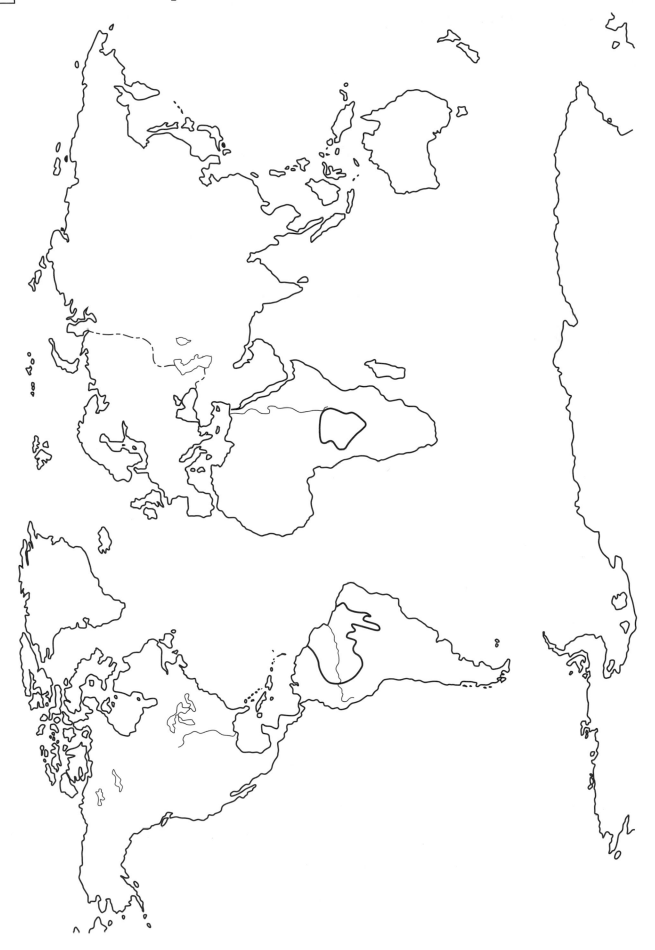

Blank map 3: Great Britain – national parks

Blank map 4: British Isles – location knowledge

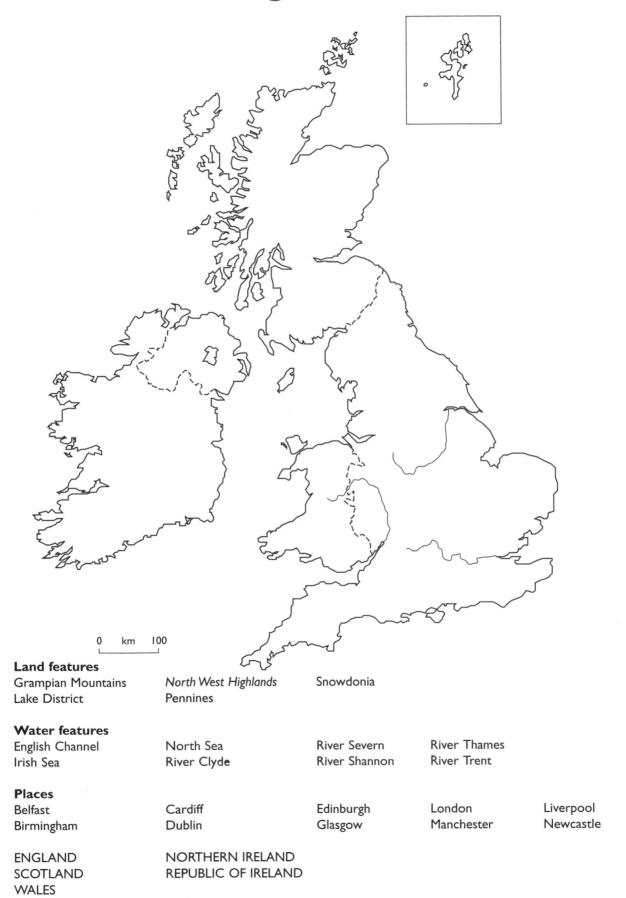

0   km   100

Land features

Grampian Mountains   *North West Highlands*   Snowdonia
Lake District   Pennines

Water features

English Channel   North Sea   River Severn   River Thames
Irish Sea   River Clyde   River Shannon   River Trent

Places

Belfast   Cardiff   Edinburgh   London   Liverpool
Birmingham   Dublin   Glasgow   Manchester   Newcastle

ENGLAND   NORTHERN IRELAND
SCOTLAND   REPUBLIC OF IRELAND
WALES

Blank map 5: Europe – location knowledge

0   km   500

Land features

Alps	*Mount Etna*	Pyrenees

Water features

Arctic Ocean	*North Atlantic Ocean*	English Channel	River Rhine

Places

Austria (Vienna)	France (Paris)	Luxembourg	*Slovakia (Bratislava)*
Belgium (Brussels)	Germany (Berlin)	(Luxembourg City)	*Slovenia (Ljubljana)*
Bulgaria (Sofia)	Greece (Athens)	*Malta (Valletta)*	Spain (Madrid)
Cyprus (Nicosia)	*Hungary (Budapest)*	Netherlands	*Sweden (Stockholm)*
Czech Republic (Prague)	Irish Republic (Dublin)	(Amsterdam)	Switzerland
Denmark (Copenhagen)	Italy (Rome)	Poland (Warsaw)	Ukraine (Kiev)
Estonia (Tallinn)	*Latvia (Riga)*	Portugal (Lisbon)	United Kingdom
Finland (Helsinki)	*Lithuania (Vilnius)*	Romania (Bucharest)	(London)
		Russia (Moscow) (not EU)	

Blank map 6: Asia – location knowledge

Land features

Himalayas

Mount Everest

Water features

Arctic Ocean

River Ganges

River Yangtze

Places

Afghanistan

Bangladesh (*Dhaka*)

China (Beijing, *Shanghai*)

Hong Kong

India (New Delhi, *Mumbai, Kolkata*)

Indonesia

Iran

Iraq

Israel

Japan (Tokyo)

Pakistan

Russia (Moscow)

Saudi Arabia

Singapore

United Arab Emirates (UAE) (Dubai)

Blank map 7: Oceania – location knowledge

Water features
River Murray-Darling
Southern Ocean

Places
Australia (*Canberra*, Sydney)
New Zealand

Blank map 8: North and Central America and the West Indies – location knowledge

0   km   1000

Land features

Hawaii   Mauna Loa   Rocky Mountains

Water features

Caribbean Sea   Mississippi River   Pacific Ocean

Places

Canada   USA (Washington DC,
Mexico (Mexico City)   Los Angeles, New York,
                                    San Francisco)

Blank map 9: South America – location knowledge

0   km   1000

Land features
Andes   *Cape Horn*

Water features
Amazon River   *South Atlantic Ocean*

Places
Argentina   *Chile*
Brazil (Rio de Janeiro,   *Peru (Lima)*
    São Paulo)*

Blank map 10: Africa – location knowledge

0   km   1000

Land features

Cape of Good Hope   Mount Kilimanjaro   Sahara Desert

Water features

Indian Ocean   River Nile   South Atlantic Ocean

Places

Egypt (Cairo)   Kenya   Mozambique   South Africa
Ethiopia   Morocco   Nigeria   Sudan

Blank map 11: World: tropical rainforests and volcanoes – location knowledge

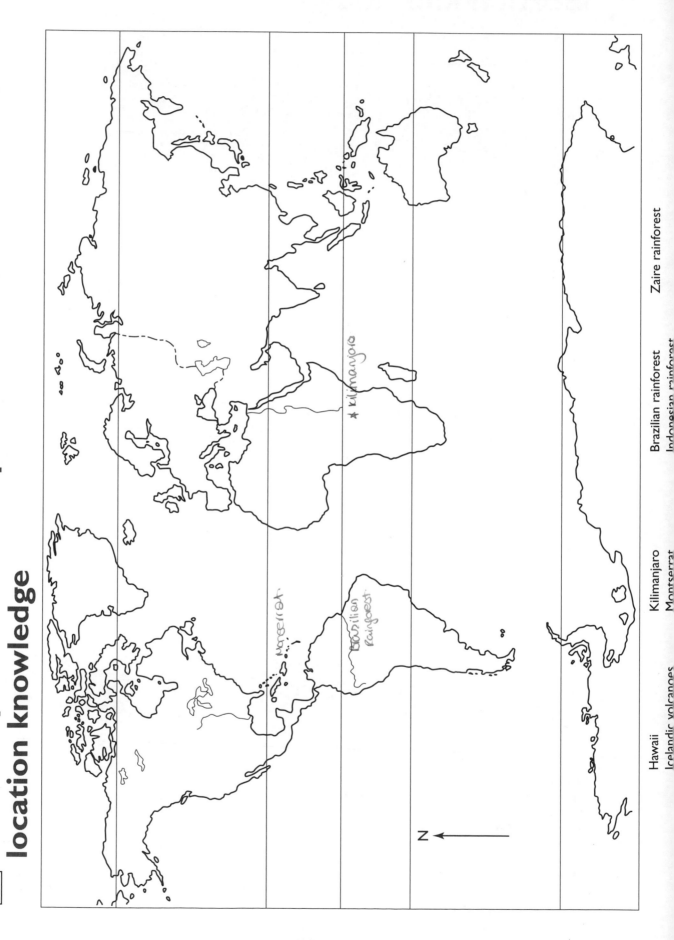

Hawaii
Icelandic volcanoes

Kilimanjaro
Montserrat

Brazilian rainforest
Indonesian rainforest

Zaire rainforest

Montserrat

Brazilian Rainforest

★ Kilimanjaro

N

Antarctic Circle
Arctic Circle
Equator
International Date Line

Latitude and Longitude
North and South Poles
Prime Meridian
Seasons

Time Zones
Tropic of Cancer
Tropic of Capricorn

Sample question answers

Chapter 1

1.1 (a) Microclimate. (1)

(b) Barometer. (1)

(c) Any three from: aspect; proximity to buildings; surfaces; distance from sea; whether in an urban or rural area. (3)

(d) The local climate will vary during the course of a bright, sunny day, depending on the physical features, surfaces and aspect. If there is a lot of tarmac, this will absorb heat throughout the day and release it at night, making night-time temperatures warm. In rural valleys, cold air will sink at night, causing frosts, which will take time to warm up through the day. A south-facing slope or wall will obviously have the benefit of the sun throughout the day so temperatures will increase from the start of the day right through to evening. (4)

1.2 A humid tropical is much hotter and wetter (convectional rainfall) and does not have a seasonal pattern of temperature. (3)

1.3 Places with humid tropical climates are near the equator, therefore the sun's rays are more concentrated, therefore they are hotter. (1)

Diagram could be included.

As humid tropical places are hotter there is rapid evaporation, which leads to convectional rainfall. (1)

Humid tropical places are on the equator and therefore they are never tilted away from or towards the sun and do not have seasonal temperatures. (1)

1.4 For an example of an extreme weather event, see cause of Hurricane Katrina on page 17.

The main points are (any six):

- Formed when a cluster of thunderstorms drifted over the warm Caribbean Sea. (1)

- The warm air from the ocean and the storm combined and rose – this created low pressure. (1)

- Trade winds blowing in opposing directions cause the storm to spin. (1)

- The rising warm air caused pressure to decrease at higher altitudes. (1)

- Air rose faster and faster to fill this low pressure, drawing more warm air off the sea and sucking cooler, drier air downwards. (1)

- The storm moved over the ocean and picked up more warm moist air. Wind speeds started to pick up as more air was sucked into the low pressure centre. (1)

- There was an eye of calm winds surrounded by a spinning vortex of high winds and heavy rain. (1)

- New Orleans is built in a bowl – Mississippi had been controlled with levees and dams for years and New Orleans was only in existence because of these. (1)

The city was suffering from subsidence as groundwater was pumped away. (1)

The coastline was disappearing. Louisiana has the highest rate of erosion in North America. (1)

Chapter 2

2.1 (i) Formation of a waterfall. (1)

(ii) A waterfall is formed when a river flowing over hard rock meets a band of softer, less resistant rock. Hydraulic action and abrasion erode the softer rock forming a 'step' in the river bed. The softer rock is undercut and the hard rock is left as overhang. A plunge pool is formed at the base of the waterfall; this plunge pool is deepened by attrition as the pebbles erode its base. (3)

2.2 The material transported in a river is the load. (1)

2.3 As the river channel moves through the drainage basin, from source to sea, the size and shape of the load alters. To start with stones roll along the bed. These stones are worn down until they become round and smooth and eventually become small particles, which 'leap-frog' along the bed. These particles become smaller and smaller until they form a suspension within the water flow, and eventually are small enough to be dissolved in the water. (3)

2.4
- Waves attack the fault by hydraulic action (sheer force of the waves hitting headland and forcing air into cracks) (1)
  and by abrasion (load being carried by wave hitting headland) (1)
  and corrosion (acids in sea water attacking headland). (1)

- Fault enlarged by the same three processes to form cave.

- Cave is widened and deepened by the same processes to form an arch.

- Undercutting, and lack of support for the arch leads to collapse, leaving a stack. (1)

- Weathering (freeze-thaw, chemical or biological) and erosion turns the stack into a stump. (1)

2.5
- A corner in the coastline, weak currents, shallow water and longshore drift are all required for spits to form. (1)

- The processes involved in spit formation are transportation (longshore drift) (1)
  and deposition. (1)

Diagram required in the answer to show how longshore drift creates spits. (2)

129

Chapter 3

3.1 Exmoor

Any four from:

- Locals and tourists will conflict as house prices and prices in shops increase, narrow roads become congested, residents' parking spaces are taken, shops and services may be more suited to tourists. (1)

- Farmers and tourists may conflict as gates are left open, trespassing occurs and livestock are scared or narrow roads become congested. (1)

- The Exmoor National Park Authority and tourists may conflict as footpaths are eroded, vegetation is trampled and litter could be dropped. (1)

- A developer may conflict with the locals and the NPA as the developer will want to make money from building hotels and 'second' homes. (1)

- Bird watchers (ornothologists) may conflict with mountain bikers as noise may disturb birds. (1)

3.2 Exmoor

Any six from:

- Building of visitor information centre at Dunster has helped educate the tourists to conserve the environment. (1)

- Green tourism leaflet encourages tourists to purchase locally produced goods, explains that they should follow the country code, engage in quiet activities and walk and use public transport rather than drive. This has the effect of boosting the sales of local farm goods and conserves the environment keeping the NPA and locals happy. (1)

- Exmoor Paths Partnership is a group of volunteers who rebuild the paths of Exmoor. This hopefully has a positive effect on the area, as areas away from the paths are less trampled and less trespassing will occur. The locals also benefit from well-maintained paths. (1)

- Developing other honeypot sites. This spreads out the economic benefits of tourism although could bring the problems associated with tourism to other parts of Exmoor. (1)

- Park and Ride system at Snowdrop Valley. This effects the place in a positive way as there is less traffic congestion on the narrow lanes and therefore less environmental pollution. The locals also benefit from less congested roads. (1)

- Conservation techniques such as culverts on Dunkery Beacon. This management technique stops the formation of gullies on Dunkery Beacon which avoids the path becoming a scar and people finding it difficult to walk on and therefore creating a new path. (1)

- Fertilizing of grass and reseeding where vegetation has been trampled. This benefits the ecosystem as vegetation can grow to bind the soil, increase infiltration, reducing soil erosion and gully formation. (1)

Chapter 4

4.1 Any two from:

- Mechanisation of farming. (1)
- Imports of food from abroad, fewer farmers in UK. (1)
- Crises in farming, e.g. Foot and Mouth. (1)
- Decline in coal mining as cheaper, cleaner, more efficient fuel becomes popular. (1)

4.2 Any three from:

- School. (1)
- Hospital. (1)
- Recreation/leisure centre. (1)
- Tourist information centre. (1)
- Any tourist feature. (1)
- Golf course. (1)

4.3 **Nike**

Any four from:

- Large market. (1)
- Advertising is everywhere, people feel they **must** get the brand, therefore number of countries with shops can expand. (1)
- In order to lower costs, manufacture happens in LEDCs as wages here are lower, (1)
  land is cheaper to buy, (1)
  the work force are more flexible and access can be gained to global markets as well as avoidance of trade restrictions. (1)
- Nike has sub-contracted factories in LEDCs to make their goods rather than build their own factories. (1)

4.4 **Nike**

Any three from:

- Headquarters – Oregon (USA). (1)
- Nike shops – mainly southern and western Europe, also Asia and North America (very few in South America or Africa). (1)
- Manufacturing – in 40 countries – clothing is mainly made in the Asia Pacific area and footwear in China, Indonesia, Vietnam and Thailand (1% of footwear is made in Italy). (1)
- No Nike clothing or footwear is made in the USA. (1)

Chapter 5

5.1
- Greater population to serve. (1)
- Therefore shops and services with high thresholds can be supported. (1)
- Tourists tend to visit cities so shops and services needed for them are required. (1)
- Office workers in cities need services associated with them. (1)
- Cities have a larger sphere of influence therefore can support more shops and services. (1)

Chapter 6

6.1 See map 9 on page 110. (1)

6.2 **Soufrière Hills volcano on Montserrat**

Any four from:

- North and South American plates met the Caribbean plate and were subducted underneath it. (1)
- This is a destructive plate boundary. (1)
- As the oceanic plates subduct the friction causes the plates to melt. (1)
- This causes excess magma which rises as it is full of gas bubbles which make it lighter than the surrounding rock. (1)
- The magma forces its way to the surface forming the Soufrière Hills Volcano. (1)

This is better answered using a well-annotated (labelled) diagram like the one on page 93.

6.3 See global location section of this book. (2)

6.4 **Soufrière Hills Volcano on Montserrat**

Any four from:

- Pyroclastic flow burned vegetation. (1)
- Ash covered two thirds of the island, (1)
  destroying agricultural land. (1)
- Coral reef and sea creatures died from the ash washed into the sea. (1)
- 60% housing destroyed. (1)
- Hospitals/schools destroyed. (1)

6.5 A – Mid-Atlantic Ridge; B – Pacific Ring of Fire.

6.6 Any three from:

- Lack of quick reaction forces to rescue people. (1)

- Poor medical care and hospitals. (1)

- Population is densely packed around a volcanic cone to benefit from the fertility of the soil. (1)

- Lack of technology and money for prediction equipment. (1)

Test yourself answers

Chapter 1

1. (a) Depression.

   (b) Any of the following: strong wind, frontal rain, changeable temperatures, cloud.

2. (a) Anticyclone.

   (b) Any of the following: very low temperatures in winter, very high temperatures in summer, no rain, very little wind, clear skies, frost, fog, stable conditions.

3. (a) Precipitation.

   (b) South-west.

   (c) An ocean current.

   (d) In winter.

   (e) Relief rainfall.

Chapter 2

1. Velocity is the **speed** of the water. Deposition is the 'dumping' of a load when the river's velocity **reduces**. Load is the material which the river **transports**. Load can be deposited by rivers at their mouth; the feature formed is called a **delta**. It is also deposited on the **inside** bend of a meander; the feature formed is called a **river beach (or slip-off slope).**

2.

	Upper course	Lower course
Size of load	large	fine
Shape of load	angular	smooth
Main methods of transportation	traction, saltation	suspension, solution

3. (a) Chemical weathering.

   (b) Freeze-thaw.

   (c) Onion-skin (exfoliation).

4. Drainage basin – an area of land drained by a river and its tributaries.

    Watershed – the boundary of the drainage basin, usually marked by a ridge of high land.

    Source – the start of the river.

    Mouth – where the river meets the sea.

    Permeable – rocks which allow water to pass through them.

    Impermeable – rock which does not allow water to pass through.

    Evaporation – the loss of water to the air when the water has turned into water vapour.

    Transpiration – the loss of moisture to the air from plants.

    Through flow – the movement of water through the soil back to the sea.

    Ground water storage – water stored in rocks below ground.

    Infiltration – the downwards movement of water through tiny pores in the soil.

    Surface run-off – the movement of water over the surface of the land back to the sea.

    River discharge – the amount of water which passes a given point at a given time, measured in cumecs.

    Load – the material which a river carries.

    Attrition – when the river's load collides and breaks into smaller pieces.

    Corrosion – a type of erosion when the acids in the river dissolve the rocks.

    Hydraulic action – a type of erosion where the force of the water breaks particles of rock from the river bank.

5. (a) Abrasion.

    (b) Corries.

    (c) Terminal moraine.

6. (a) A – arête/pyramidal peak/horn.

        B – corrie lake.

        C – rock lip.

    (b) Plucking (a form of erosion) on the back walls of two corries which back onto each other. The backwalls of the corries retreat leaving a narrow ridge separating them. This could be shown diagrammatically.

Chapter 3

1. Development which uses resources in a way which means they will not run out.

2. A rural area with rare or beautiful landscape, which needs to be protected from development. For example the Lake District.

or

An area containing rare plants, animals and landscapes, designated by the government as worthy of needing special conservation. For example the Lake District.

3. To protect rare plants, animals and landscapes from development. To preserve local jobs, culture and ways of life. To encourage people from urban areas to visit and enjoy the countryside.

Chapter 4

1. A service industry selling goods or providing a service.

2. The way in which companies, ideas and lifestyle are spreading more and more around the world.

3. A company which has branches in many countries.

Chapter 5

1. A city with a population of over 10 million.

2. Commercial; offices; shops; services; leisure; theatres; cinemas; restaurants; transport nodes (train/bus station); cathedral.

3. In the 1950s the Docklands was one of the **busiest** ports in the world. Ships on the River Thames transported wood, coal and food. New forms of **transportation** which were more efficient were invented, ships became too large to sail up the Thames and goods were transported in huge containers; the area declined and there was high **unemployment**. The London Docklands Development Corporation was set up to try to alleviate the problems. It attracted new **industry** and improved the transport links as well as creating new flats. It also improved many of the services and created **parkland**. However the LDDC has suffered much criticism in that the new jobs created required **skills** which the ex-dockers did not have. The new **luxury** flats were too expensive for the locals. The feeling between the newcomers and the original residents was uneasy. The ex-dockers felt that more care could have been put into creating jobs, housing and **services** which are more suitable to their needs.

Chapter 6

1. The Pacific Ring of Fire.

2. Shield volcanoes.

3. A tiltmeter.